Pooh and Piglet walked home thoughtfully together in the
golden evening, and for a long time they were silent.

"When you wake up in the morning, Pooh," said Piglet at last,
"what's the first thing you say to yourself?"

"What's for breakfast?" said Pooh. "What do you say, Piglet?"

"I say, I wonder what's going to happen
exciting today?" said Piglet.

Pooh nodded thoughtfully.

"It's the same thing," he said.

— *A.A. Milne, Winnie the Pooh*

"'Bulk Devan up,' we were told as our skinny four-year-old son faced chemotherapy and a bone marrow transplant following relapsed leukemia. Chemo does strange things. In the hospital, mac'n'cheese seemed to satisfy Devan during the transplant and somehow we all made it through that time. Now I cook a varied, healthy, high-calorie diet and he hasn't touched mac'n'cheese since."

— *Dermot T, father, and Devan, age 6, Leukemia (APL)*

DONOR ACKNOWLEDGEMENTS

This book would not have been possible had it not been for the generous support of the following donors. The first of its kind for pediatric cancer patients, we hope this book will fulfill its purpose, which is, teach the importance of healthy nutrition to patients, their families and cancer survivors. We are deeply indebted to you.

Bryce Foundation: To Emily and James Anderson, who made this gift in loving remembrance of their son Bryce. Bryce Foundation (www.BryceFoundation.org) advocates for healthy nutrition in cancer patients and has been a long-time supporter of MedStar Georgetown University Hospital's Division of Pediatric Hematology/Oncology through its Healthy Meals program as well as other Bryce Foundation projects.

Mary and Jeff Lane: who, for many years have been strong supporters of the Division of Pediatric Hematology/Oncology at MedStar Georgetown University Hospital. Mary has been closely involved in the production of this book from the very start.

Michelle, Steve, Jessica and Ryan Bosch: One short lunchtime conversation and a discussion on cancer nutrition was all it took for Michelle to declare her enthusiastic support for this project. Thank you!

Enterprise Holdings Foundation: We thank you for recognizing the value and need for such a book for young cancer patients and survivors.

Acknowledgments

When you come from an extended family named Cook, most of whom are avid if not passionate cooks, you're going to get a lot of help and advice on this kind of a project. Beyond the constructive support of a loving family were many key people who made this project possible.

Aziza T. Shad, MD, Amey Distinguished Professor of Neuro-Oncology and Childhood Cancer and Director, Division of Pediatric Hematology Oncology and BMT, MedStar Georgetown University Hospital, Lombardi Comprehensive Cancer Center, to whom we were referred when Fabien became ill, has been his and every young cancer patient's unconditional advocate. She believes deeply in the value of good nutrition and in this project, and I am most grateful we can see this first book come to fruition. The doctors, nurses, aides, administrative staff and all the families at The Children's Cancer Foundation Pediatric Hematology Oncology Clinic, MedStar Georgetown University Hospital, who tasted, critiqued and talked with me about food, thank you for the feedback. Tim Mooney, Mary Lane, Jan Powers, Tracy Council, you enthusiastically endorsed this project and helped to move it forward.

A heartfelt thank you to Kathy Horn of Blue Skies Studio for the graphic design; to Kevin Allen of Kevin Allen Photography; and to Shanishka Bain, my fellow Hawthorn University nutrition student, for all her nutritional analysis help. To the Hawthorn faculty who encouraged this project throughout, I believe the knowledge I have learned from the masters program has helped combine the science of food with the pleasure of cooking.

— *Danielle Cook Navidi*

Danielle Navidi: mother, nutritionist and chef— all rolled into one! Her creativity, perseverance, understanding of cancer nutrition and commitment to children with cancer and their families is single-handedly responsible for the success of our Cooking for Cancer program and this amazing cookbook *Happily Hungry*. It has been a privilege working with her on this project and along the way I think I may have become a better cook as well!

Amal Abu-Ghosh, MD, Fabien's oncologist, for all the personalized care she gave him.

Kathy Horn, graphic designer, who brought this book to life through her artistic and vivid presentation of the recipes and other contents.

Tim Mooney and Mary Lane for their untiring support and personal interest at every step in the evolution of this book.

To all the children and families battling cancer, whose enthusiastic participation in the production of *Happily Hungry* has made this book so meaningful and personal. I hope it can help alleviate some of your stress related to meals and serve as a guide to healthy living!

— *Aziza T. Shad, MD*

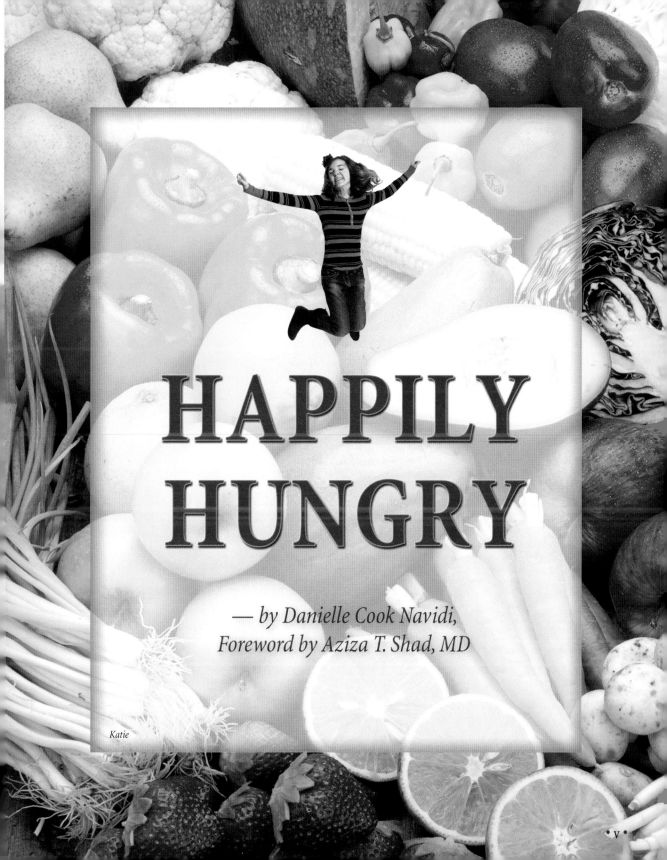

HAPPILY HUNGRY

— by Danielle Cook Navidi,
Foreword by Aziza T. Shad, MD

Katie

For more information about MedStar Georgetown University Hospital/
Lombardi Comprehensive Cancer Center, Division of Pediatric Hematology/Oncology, please
visit lombardi.georgetown.edu/pediatric

For more information about MedStar Georgetown University Hospital, please
visit medstargeorgetown.org

For more information about MedStar Georgetown University Hospital's Department of Pediatrics,
please visit medstargeorgetown.org/pediatrics

For more information about Danielle Cook Navidi, please visit pomegranate-plus.com

Printed by Walsworth Printers

MEDICAL DISCLAIMER FOR
HAPPILY HUNGRY: SMART RECIPES FOR KIDS WITH CANCER

The ideas, recipes and concepts expressed in *Happily Hungry: Smart Recipes for Kids with Cancer* are intended to be used for educational purposes only. This book is sold with the understanding that the author and publisher are not rendering medical advice of any kind, nor is this book intended to replace medical advice, nor to diagnose, prescribe or treat any disease, condition, metabolic disorder, health problem, illness or injury.

It is imperative that before beginning any nutrition program, including any aspect of *Happily Hungry: Smart Recipes for Kids with Cancer,* you receive full medical clearance from a licensed physician.

The authors and publisher claim no responsibility to any person or entity for any liability, loss or damage caused or alleged to be caused directly or indirectly as a result of the use, application or interpretation of the material in this book.

The Food and Drug Administration has not evaluated the statements/recipes contained in the *Happily Hungry: Smart Recipes for Kids with Cancer.*

GROUP, Page iii, holding signs: "T," Katie, age 13, Leukemia (AML/BMT); "H," Zoe, age 13, Leukemia (Pre-B ALL); "AN," Ashley, age 15, Hodgkin's Lymphoma; "K," Sophie, age 7, Neuroblastoma; "Y," Alex, age 14, Aplastic Anemia; "OU," Simone, age 9, Brain Tumor (Pilocytic Astrocytoma); "D," Ayden, age 5, Leukemia (Pre-B ALL); "O," Destinee, age 6, Leukemia (T ALL); "N," Ali, age 7, Aplastic Anemia; "O," Peter, age 6, Leukemia (Pre-B ALL); "RS," Brandon, age 5, Lymphoblastic Lymphoma

Table of Contents

From the Author: Danielle Cook Navidi 2

Foreword: Aziza T. Shad, MD 4

Introduction: Fabien Navidi-Kasmai 5

Chapter 1: Smoothies and Soothing Beverages 7

Chapter 2: Snacks and Little People Bites 17

Chapter 3: Better in a Bowl: Broths and Soups 25

Chapter 4: We Need a Little Comfort: Dishes for All Moods and Matters 35

Chapter 5: Digestion: Easy-to-Eat Sides 45

Chapter 6: Vibrant and Vital Veggies 57

Chapter 7: Satisfying Sweets and Desserts 65

Recipe Cross-Reference Chart 74

Suggestions to Treat Side Effects 76

Bibliography and Recommended Reading 77

Index 78

Throughout this book you will see the following abbreviations as a reference to which side effects each recipe helps aid. See pages 74–75 for a recipe cross-reference list.

Nausea/Appetite Loss	(N/AL)
Constipation	(C)
Mouth Sores, Difficulty Swallowing	(MS/DS)
Fatigue	(F)
Neutropenia	(N)
Taste Alterations	(TA)

—Danielle Cook Navidi

I t was my son, Fabien, who said it. We were sitting around the dinner table like many other families. But we weren't like any other family because a few months prior, we received the devastating diagnosis that Fabien, our 11-year-old, had Hodgkin's lymphoma, Stage III. The weeks and months of stress and turbulence that followed in his treatment included surgery, chemotherapy, radiation, blood transfusions, endless scans, and finally, remission. Here we were, our family of five intact, and somehow we had made it through the storm. He said, "This is my new favorite soup, Mom. It tastes like someone is taking care of me."

His words, sweet and simple, took on a new meaning for me. There was actual truth to what he said. We've heard "You are what you eat," or rather, my preference, "You are what they ate." Food is an integral part of all cultures and there is science behind why some foods are good for us and others are not. I pondered why people get cravings for certain foods, why others cannot tolerate some foods and why we find comfort in familiar dishes. And then, when the months of treatment were over and we were all home with no more hospital stays on the horizon, the work of healing, restoring health—both physical and psychological—began. There was no prescription for that, I learned quickly. So on instinct and a lot of reading and research on my own, I began to rebuild the tired, worn, depressed body of my young cancer survivor. I took care of him with soups, broths, vegetables, dishes from ancient times and modern times, and experimented with new ways to satisfy sweet cravings. This commitment to healing him with foods led me to pursue a master of science in nutrition, and to teach cooking classes and conduct cooking demonstrations in numerous venues, including botanical gardens, schools and at The Children's Cancer Foundation Pediatric Hematology Oncology Clinic, MedStar Georgetown University Hospital. Here at the hospital, we launched a unique nutrition program that teaches and counsels pediatric oncology patients and their families about the benefits of healthy food choices.

This book was designed for the little ones fighting hard to get well again, for families and caregivers whose child is in or has completed cancer treatment, and for those looking for healthful, smart food choices appealing to kids' tastes. At a time when every bite counts, it is often impossible to coax even the smallest spoonful into the patient. Knowing what to shop for, what to cook, or how to identify the right kinds of foods that will best support this difficult time is an added challenge. And yet, success-ful cancer treatment is dependent on a patient who is prepared to stay on schedule. Eating well, drinking healthful broths, teas, smoothies and soups all are integral parts of the treatment and recovery protocol. Treatment causes nausea, impaired taste buds, weakness and pain, fatigue, dehydration, mouth and throat sores, immune-compromised issues, weight loss and a damaged digestive system. Flavor, smell, color, texture and the hidden gems of optimal nutrition must come together and begin the magical powers of healing.

Danielle Cook Navidi

Foreword

The role of nutrition in cancer cannot be over-emphasized. While good nutrition and healthy food choices should be an integral part of every individual's daily life, maintaining appropriate nutrition during cancer treatment is crucial, especially for a child.

Each year over 12,000 children under the age of 20 are diagnosed with cancer in the U.S. The cancer and its treatment—chemotherapy, radiation and surgery—can cause change in taste, appetite loss, mucositis, nausea, vomiting and aversion to food.

Healthy nutrition makes treatment more tolerable and decreases susceptibility to infection. It correlates positively with shorter hospitalizations, fewer complications and lower cost of care. Good nutrition promotes normal growth and development during and after completion of therapy, and minimizes late effects such as obesity. For cancer survivors, an appropri-

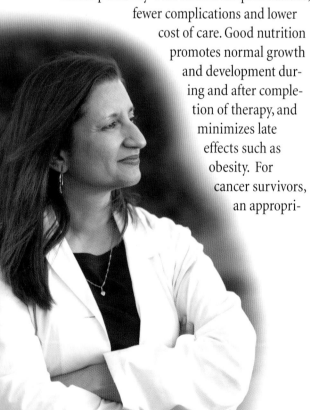

ate weight, healthy diet and a physically active lifestyle are integral for preventing recurrence, second cancers and other chronic diseases.

Families of children with cancer often perceive a lack of control of their situation and look for ways to support their child. Ensuring adequate nutrition is one of the few ways in which parents can participate in their child's treatment. Such is the story of Danielle Navidi and her son Fabien. Her strong desire to heal her son after his treatment ended sparked her interest in healthy nutrition and inspired her to become a holistic nutritionist.

Today, Danielle directs our highly innovative pediatric oncology nutrition program, "Cooking for Cancer". Supported by a grant from "Hyundai Hope on Wheels," the program includes assessment, instruction, cooking demonstrations and education promoting healthy eating during and after cancer treatment.

This amazing collection of Danielle's unique recipes, *Happily Hungry: Smart Recipes for Kids with Cancer* is the first of its kind for children with cancer and their families. Filled with excellent nutritional information, suggestions and tips, along with recipes appealing to kids' tastes, it belongs in the kitchen of anyone whose life has been touched by cancer.

— *Aziza T. Shad, MD*
Amey Distinguished Professor of Neuro-Oncology
*   and Childhood Cancer*
Director, Pediatric Hematology Oncology,
Blood and Marrow Transplantation
MedStar Georgetown University Hospital
Lombardi Comprehensive Cancer Center
Washington, D.C.

Introduction

In Farsi, they call yogurt "mast."

It isn't spelled like that though, because well, people who speak Farsi write in Farsi, but it's pronounced like "must." From a young age I've loved mast. My grandma would dice cucumbers and put them in mast, we would put mast on rice, and add honey to mast as a sweet, healthy dessert. I've even been told stories about how when I was two years old I would demand "more mast!" and my American grandfather would keel over laughing.

When I was 11, cancer brought the relationship to a whole new level of commitment. Chemotherapy ripped apart my stomach, to the point that I could no longer eat breakfast in the morning or enjoy a delicious slice of lasagna because of the acidity of tomatoes (which was quite a tragedy because I also love lasagna). However mast remained loyal to my intestines, never causing an argument and gently comforting my throat when I had the appetite for a bowl. It was a cold, soothing snack for when my body was sent into hot flashes because of Vincristine, and an easy bit of nutrition after being pumped full of Zofran to attempt to control nausea. And in all honesty, it was a motivating amount of probiotics when I was declared medically F.O.S. (Full Of S...tool).

It's hard to eat during chemo, because when you aren't throwing up, you're not necessarily hungry either. The times you do want to eat become extremely valuable, and you have to take advantage of the appetite. I didn't realize it at the time, but craving mast made complete sense—my insides were a battlefield and yogurt was the perfect way to put out the fire. To this day I love yogurt, and would take a bowl of it over nearly any other treat anytime. In my battle against cancer, mast was a must.

— *Fabien Navidi-Kasmai, age 19,*
Hodgkin's Lymphoma

TIP ·····

If neutropenia is an issue, replace all the fresh fruit with frozen fruit and fresh herbs with dried. Frozen fruits are always a great option, since the fruit is picked at the height of ripeness and nutritional power.

Chapter 1

Smoothies and Soothing Beverages

At The Children's Cancer Foundation Pediatric Hematology Oncology Clinic, MedStar Georgetown University Hospital, a new program called Cooking for Cancer features cooking demonstrations, healthy food choices and nutrition consultation for young cancer patients and their families. Kids enjoy tasting new things brought into the clinic, and they especially get a kick out of the featured "Smoothie of the Month." Here are a few of the patients' hands-down favorites. None of the smoothies and beverages contains sugar, but they are sweet. These drinks will help a stressed digestive system, and because the ingredients do not require chewing, the nutrition will absorb more quickly into the body. You may even find that after a few tentative sips, the patient will be back for more.

Purple Power Smoothie

1/2 banana
1/2 cup fresh or frozen blueberries
1/2 cup açai-blueberry juice
1/4 cup soft silken tofu
1/4 cup plain or vanilla soy milk
Squeeze of lemon juice, to taste
Agave nectar, to taste

Process all ingredients in a blender until smooth.
Makes 1 (17-ounce) smoothie.

Nutritional info: Calories: 311; Total Fat: 5.4g;
Protein: 10g; Carbohydrates: 60g; Sugars: 46g.

(MS/DS) (F) (N) (N/AL)

TIP ·····

Agave nectar is a natural, plant-based sweetener made from several varieties of the agave plant, which tequila comes from. The milky juice from the inside of the plant is collected, cleaned and filtered to become agave nectar. No processing chemicals are ever used in the production, making it a completely safe and organic sweetener. Agave nectars are low-glycemic sweeteners, and are well suited for diabetics and those concerned about blood-sugar levels during chemotherapy.

Mango Lassi

1 cup plain yogurt, whole milk or low fat
1/4 cup milk, whole or low fat
1 cup fresh or frozen mango chunks
Agave nectar or honey, to taste
Pinch of cardamom, for garnish (optional)

Process all ingredients in a blender until smooth.
Makes 1 (17-ounce) smoothie. Keeps up to 24
hours in the refrigerator, reblend before serving.

Nutritional info: Calories: 360; Total Fat: 6g;
Protein: 15.6g; Carbohydrates: 65g; Sugars: 62g.

(MS/DS) (F) (N) (N/AL)

TIP ·····

Soy yogurt and soy milk
can be substituted to
make this dairy-free.

Succulent Strawberry-Banana Smoothie

1/2 banana
1/2 cup fresh or frozen strawberries
1/2 cup berry juice
1/4 cup soft silken tofu
Squeeze of lemon juice, to taste
Agave nectar, to taste

Process all ingredients in a blender until smooth. Makes 1 (13-ounce) smoothie.

Nutritional info: Calories: 277; Total Fat: 3.1g; Protein: 4.5g; Carbohydrates: 63g; Sugars: 34g.

(MS/DS) (F) (N/AL)

Ginger or Galangal Ale*

2 cups fresh ginger or
   galangal, cut into thick pieces (unpeeled)
6 cups water
1/4–1/2 cup agave nectar, to taste
1 tablespoon fresh lemon juice
Seltzer water, chilled
1 cup fresh or frozen grapes or blueberries

Combine the ginger or galangal and water in a large pot. Bring to a boil, reduce heat and simmer with a lid slightly ajar for about 1 hour, or until reduced by one third. Let cool. Strain off the ginger or galangal; add lemon juice and agave nectar to taste. Store in the refrigerator until ready to use.

   To serve pour 1/4 cup of the ginger syrup in a glass, add cold seltzer water and garnish with fresh or frozen grapes or blueberries.

Nutritional info (1/4 cup syrup): Calories: 50; Total Fat: 0g; Protein: 0g; Carbohydrates: 13g; Sugars: 11g.

(N/AL) (TA) (N)

> **TIP** ·····
>
> Nausea-reducing, anti-inflammatory and antibacterial properties are some of the wonderful benefits of ginger. Ginger contains gingerol, a very potent compound which helps reduce inflammation. It's also known for its ability to relax the intestinal tract and reduce intestinal gas, thereby alleviating symptoms of gastrointestinal distress.

*adapted from Rebecca Katz, **Cancer-Fighting Kitchen***

Watermelon Slushie

1 1/2 cups cubed fresh watermelon
1/2 cup unsweetened decaffeinated green tea
1/4 cup fresh mint leaves, washed and stems removed (or 1 tablespoon dried)
Agave nectar, to taste

Freeze the watermelon overnight in a medium plastic container. Combine frozen watermelon, green tea, mint and a dash of agave. Puree until thick and smooth. Serve immediately. Makes 1 (13-ounce) slushie.

Nutritional info: Calories: 200; Total Fat: 0g; Protein: 1.6g; Carbohydrates: 53g; Sugars: 49g.

(N/AL) (TA) (N) (C) (F)

TIP ·····

This is a great way to rehydrate a depleted body, and the mint helps stimulate an appetite.

TIP ·····

A refreshing change of pace from other beverages, the flavors come together with the sweet honeydew and tart lime, aided by the juicy grapes.

Honeydew Lime Cooler

1 1/2 cups cubed fresh honeydew melon
1/2 cup seedless red or green grapes
1/4 cup fresh squeezed lime juice
1/4 cup honey, to taste
1 cup seltzer water

Freeze the honeydew and grapes for at least 1 hour. Combine the frozen melon and grapes with lime juice and honey in a blender. Puree until smooth, adding seltzer water as needed. Serve immediately. Makes 1 (14-ounce) cooler.

Nutritional info: Calories: 265; Total Fat: 0g; Protein: 2g; Carbohydrates: 71g; Sugars: 64g.

(N/AL) (TA) (N)

Orange-Cream Freeze

1 cup fresh squeezed orange juice
1/4 cup plain yogurt, whole milk or low fat
1/4 cup milk, whole or low fat
Agave nectar, to taste

(N/AL) (TA) (N)

TIP ·····

Turn this into a dairy-free treat by substituting soy milk and yogurt for the milk and yogurt.

Combine orange juice, yogurt and milk in a blender. Pulse to puree until creamy. Adjust for sweetness. Freeze mixture for 1 hour, stirring every 15 minutes until smooth. If frozen hard, let warm slightly and spoon into a bowl. Makes 1 (14-ounce) freeze.

Nutritional info: Calories: 250; Total Fat: 4.5g; Protein: 5.8g; Carbohydrates: 49g; Sugars: 44g.

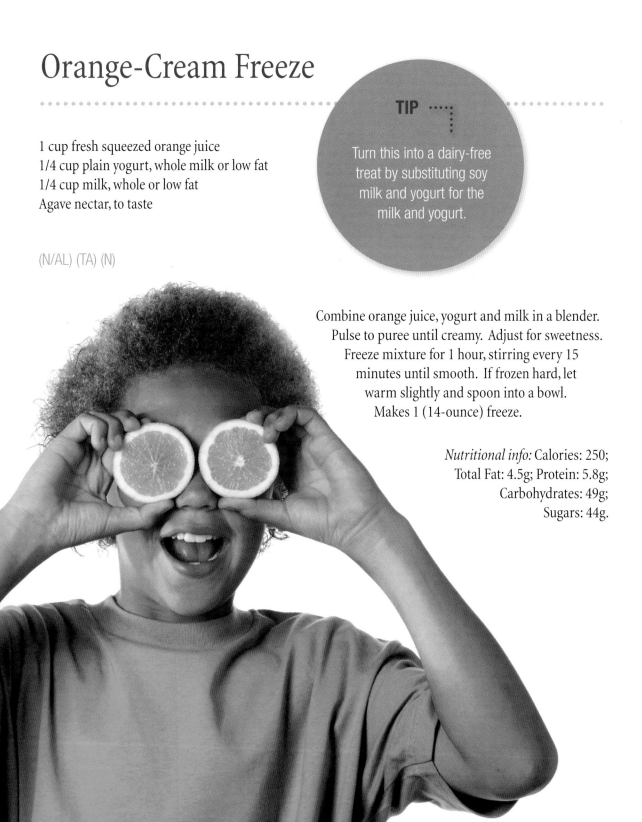

"At a time when worry fogged my mind and fear paralyzed my ability to prepare my usual meals, and neck radiation prevented my son from eating, Danielle's fruit smoothie recipes literally saved us. It became the base and start of simple, nutritious liquid meals. What a blessing for this book to be born, with simple, easily accessible recipes. For families undergoing treatment, there is no other cancer cookbook like it!"

— Vicky S, mother, and Chris, age 19, Nasopharyngeal Carcinoma

Anuj, age 4, Hemophagocytic Lymphohistiocytosis (HLH)

Chapter 2

Snacks and Little People Bites

Sometimes nibbling here and there is as much as a young patient can manage, and that's better than eating nothing. Keeping snacks with you as you move from appointment to appointment can delay hunger, balance blood sugar levels and mood swings, and stave off nausea and boredom. Here are a few healthful options, sweet and savory, that are not limited to the patient—siblings, parents and caregivers can all participate in the making, baking and nibbling.

Lemon-Lime Yogurt Muffins

1 1/4 cups oat or organic unbleached flour
3/4 teaspoon baking powder
1/4 teaspoon salt
1/8 teaspoon baking soda
1/8 teaspoon ground nutmeg
1/4 cup lemon-flavored yogurt
2 tablespoons minced fresh lemon
1/2 teaspoon vanilla extract
6 tablespoons natural sugar, preferably
    maple sugar or evaporated cane sugar
1/2 stick unsalted butter, softened
1 egg
1/4 cup natural sugar, preferably maple
    sugar or evaporated cane sugar
Zest of 1 lime
3 tablespoons unsalted butter, melted

Preheat oven to 350°F. Prepare one 12-cup mini muffin pan or 6 standard-size muffin pan with non-stick spray or muffin wrappers.

Whisk together the flour, baking powder, salt, baking soda and nutmeg. In a separate bowl, blend the yogurt, minced lemon and vanilla. (NOTE: to mince the lemon, cut the fruit into chunks, remove the seeds and pulse the entire lemon in a food processor until it is the texture of oatmeal).

Cream the butter with the sugar until light and fluffy. Add the egg, beat well. Alternately add the flour mixture and the yogurt mixture into the butter. Do not over mix. Fill the muffin pan cups three-quarters full, bake until a toothpick inserted in a muffin comes out clean, about 20–25 minutes. Cool briefly in the pan.

Pulse 1/4 cup sugar with the lime zest in a food processor until the zest is well minced. Brush muffins with 3 tablespoons melted butter and roll in sugar mixture to coat. Makes 6 standard muffins or 12 mini muffins.

Nutritional info (1 standard muffin): Calories: 279; Total Fat: 14.8g; Protein: 5g; Carbohydrates: 34g; Sugars: 14.5g.

(C) (F) (N) (TA) (N/AL)

TIP ·····

Oat, spelt, barley and coconut flours are more nutritious than refined white flour. Widely available in grocery and health food stores, these and other gluten-free flours have become a popular option to unbleached white.

Carrot Coconut Walnut Muffins

2 cups oat flour
1/2 cup coconut flour
2 teaspoons baking soda
1 teaspoon sea salt
1 teaspoon ground cinnamon
1/4 teaspoon ground nutmeg
1/4 teaspoon ground allspice
1/4 teaspoon ground cloves
1 cup natural sugar, preferably maple
   sugar or evaporated cane sugar
4 eggs
1 cup olive oil
4 cups grated carrots (4–5 medium-sized)
1/2 cup dried currants
1 cup walnuts, chopped
1/2 cup dried unsweetened coconut

(C) (F) (N)

TIP

These muffins taste better after they sit for a day—the flavors and olive oil meld nicely. A definite kid favorite, these muffins are just sweet enough, filling and satisfying whether you're on the go or just need a little lift. Walnuts are an excellent source of heart-healthy monounsaturated fats.

Preheat oven to 350°F. Prepare two 12-cup standard-size muffin pans, or two 24 mini-size muffin pans with non-stick spray or muffin wrappers.

Mix the first 9 ingredients in a bowl. In a separate bowl, whisk together the eggs and the oil. Stir the wet ingredients into the dry, mixing well until the dry ingredients are moistened. Add the carrots, currants, walnuts and coconut. The batter will be very thick and dense. Use an ice cream scooper to fill the muffin pans almost to the top of the wrappers or pan. Bake 25 minutes or until a toothpick inserted in a muffin comes out dry. Cool thoroughly. Makes 18–24 standard muffins.

Nutritional info (1 standard muffin):
Calories: 318; Total Fat: 22g; Protein: 5.6g;
Carbohydrates: 27g; Sugars: 11g.

Savory Crustless Popovers

TIP ·····

A good source of protein and healthy fats, these popovers are great to make and take along. Since the herbs also get cooked, this is an ideal snack food when the patient is neutropenic.

3 eggs
2/3 cup half and half
1/2 cup plain lowfat yogurt
1 tablespoon unsalted butter, melted
1/3 cup oat or organic unbleached flour
1/2 teaspoon sea salt
4 ounces mild cheddar, shredded
2 tablespoons EACH fresh parsley and
    chives, finely chopped

Preheat oven to 400°F. Butter a standard 12-cup muffin tin (or a 24-cup mini-muffin tin, or ramekins) well, making sure to grease the sides as well as the base of each cup.

Whisk together the eggs, half and half, yogurt and butter. Add the flour and salt, stir in the cheddar and herbs. Fill greased tins 3/4 full and bake for 20 minutes, or until set, puffy and lightly brown on top. Let popovers cool at least 10 minutes before unmolding. (They will fall slightly, this is normal!) Gently invert to unmold. Serve warm or at room temperature. Makes 12 standard muffins.

Nutritional info: Calories: 100; Total Fat: 7g; Protein: 5g; Carbohydrates: 4g; Sugars: 0g.

(MS/DS) (F) (N)

Traditional Cucumber Raita

1 cup plain yogurt
1/2 cucumber, peeled and grated
2 tablespoons fresh mint, finely chopped
   (or 2 teaspoons dried)
1/2 teaspoon sea salt
Pinch of cayenne pepper (optional)

Put the yogurt in a bowl and stir lightly until smooth and creamy.
Add the grated cucumber, mint and salt. Stir well, adjust for taste.
Let mixture sit at least 30 minutes and up to several hours, refrigerated, until ready to serve. Serve on its own in little bowls or with
pita chips. Serves 2–4.

Nutritional info: Calories: 58; Total Fat: 2.7g; Protein: 3.2g;
Carbohydrates: 5.7g; Sugars: 4.6g.

(N/AL) (MS/DS) (F)

TIP ·····

Many cultures have their own
version of cucumber-yogurt
dips, and one isn't any more
or less authentic than the next.
Dried mint is fine to use in this
recipe, while other versions
include a touch of dried
tarragon as well as a combination of mint, dill, oregano and
thyme. Some recipes also
call for finely minced onion
or garlic. There are two key
components in this dip that are
the nutritional source for the
patient: the yogurt, which helps
with stomach acidity and is an
excellent source of live cultures,
and cucumber, for its vitamin C
and cooling and rehydrating
effects.

Pleasing Peanut Butter Dip with Fruit and Veggie Stix

1/2 cup organic peanut butter
4 ounces cream cheese, softened at room temperature for 30 minutes
2–3 tablespoons milk
2 teaspoons honey

Beat the cream cheese and peanut butter together with an electric mixer or wooden spoon. Add 2 table-spoons of milk, the honey, and mix well. Add more milk if necessary to achieve desired consistency. Serve with an assortment of "dippers" such as apples, celery, carrots, jicama, pear slices or pita chips. Serves 4.

Nutritional info: Calories: 278; Total Fat: 24.5g; Protein: 9.0g; Carbohydrates: 9.2g; Sugars: 6g.

(C) (F) (TA)

TIP

Why buy organic peanut butter? Peanuts are often grown as a rotation crop with cotton and sometimes with tobacco. These are heavily sprayed crops, hence a concern for carcinogens. Peanuts are an excellent source of boron, a trace mineral that plays an important role in bone health. They are also an excellent source of protein and fat, B vitamins and tryptophan, an amino acid that promotes a healthy nervous system.

"As a family, we have gone through a sea change in the way that we eat. Cookbooks replace the coffee maker and sprouted seeds replace dry roasted nuts. To help change the way that we eat, we have sought out like-minded people and challenged our mind set. Natural? What does that mean? Once you realize that you can help your body mend itself or achieve a physical challenge (we are all athletes) by fueling it properly, the quest to find the best food to do that becomes a mainstream goal and not just a weird passion."

— *Gerry L, father, and Bella, age 16, Neuro-endocrine tumor*

Chapter 3

Better in a Bowl: Broths and Soups

There's nothing more comforting than a bowl of homemade soup on a cold day, hot day, bad day, good day. It's the perfect food at any time, and it may be the one food that carries the patient and caregivers through treatment. Do yourself the favor of making your own chicken broth, it will serve you well on many fronts. Not only will the fabulous smell fill the house, it will stimulate appetites and you'll have everyone wanting more. A good broth is the foundation for great soups, and the broth on its own may be just what the doctor ordered. A rich chicken broth, simply seasoned with a little lemon juice, sea salt or Tamari sauce, can do wonders for an unhappy child.

Homemade Chicken Broth

TIP ·····

Once the broth has simmered for 2–3 hours, you can carefully lift the breast meat off the chicken with the help of kitchen tongs. Let the broth continue to cook another few hours with the remaining carcass. Use the delicious poached chicken in sandwiches or enjoy it on its own, or use in chicken noodle soup.

I (3–4 pound) free-range chicken
1 yellow onion, unpeeled and cut in half
2 medium carrots, cut into thirds
2 large celery stalks, cut into thirds
1 small bunch fresh parsley (with stems), rinsed
1 tablespoon Herbes de Provence (or substitute
    with 1 teaspoon each thyme, marjoram, basil)
2 bay leaves
1 teaspoon whole black peppercorns
8 quarts water

Put all the ingredients in a large stockpot. Cover in cold water to 2 inches from the rim. Bring to a gentle boil on medium heat, reduce heat and let simmer uncovered for at least 2 hours. As the water evaporates, add more and continue simmering for another 4–6 hours. The broth is ready to use, or you can let it cool overnight and then strain it through a large colander or sieve. Once thoroughly chilled, the fat will rise to the top of the pot and you should skim it off before using. Store the broth in airtight containers in the refrigerator for 4–5 days or in the freezer for up to 3 months. Makes 6 quarts.

(N/AL) (C) (MS/DS) (F) (N) (TA)

Nutritional info (8 ounces): Calories: 94; Total Fat: 0g; Protein: 7g; Carbohydrates: 0g; Sugars: 0g.

Kids' Favorite Chicken Noodle Soup

1 tablespoon olive oil
1/2 tablespoon butter
1 medium carrot, diced
1 celery stalk, diced
1 shallot or small onion, minced
1 teaspoon turmeric
1 tablespoon rice flour
4–5 cups homemade chicken broth
   (recipe at left)
1/2 cup alphabet or vermicelli noodles
   (Eden Organic Alphabets preferred)
1 teaspoon agave nectar
Fresh lemon juice to taste
Salt and pepper to taste

(N/AL) (C) (MS/DS) (F) (N) (TA)

TIP ·····

Organic, low-sodium chicken broth can be substituted for homemade. Get another punch of nutrition by adding 6 ounces of fresh baby spinach just before you ladle up the soup.

In a medium-sized pot over medium heat, melt the butter with the olive oil. When the butter begins to bubble add the carrot, celery and shallots. Sauté until the vegetables begin to soften, about 4 minutes. Sprinkle in the turmeric, then add the flour and cook for another minute, until the flour is well-absorbed into the vegetables. Add 1 cup of chicken broth and stir well. Add the remaining broth, the pasta, lemon juice and agave. Bring to a gentle simmer for 20 minutes. Adjust taste for salt, pepper and more lemon, if necessary. Serves 4.

Nutritional info: Calories: 302; Total Fat: 10g; Protein: 5.7g; Carbohydrates: 55g; Sugars: 16g.

Creamy Tomato Soup Topped with Zucchini "Croutons"

1 cup sweet onion, chopped (about 1 medium)

2 cloves garlic, minced

2 medium carrots, diced

3 tablespoons butter

2 1/2 pounds ripe tomatoes (about three very large), core removed and diced large, or may substitute 3 15-ounce cans of diced tomatoes

1 teaspoon agave nectar

1 teaspoon sea salt

1 1/2 cups chicken broth, preferably homemade

1/2 cup dry white wine

1/2 cup heavy cream

1/2 cup fresh basil leaves, chopped

FOR THE ZUCCHINI "CROUTONS"

1 1/2 pounds zucchini (about 3 medium), diced

4 tablespoons butter

(N/AL) (C) (MS/DS) (F) (N) (TA)

Melt 3 tablespoons of butter in a 6-quart sauce pan over medium-high heat. Add the onion and carrots and cook until onions become translucent, about 3–4 minutes. Add the garlic and sauté another minute or two. Increase the heat, add the tomatoes, agave nectar and salt and cook, stirring constantly for about a minute, until the tomatoes begin to bubble. Add the chicken broth and wine (the alcohol from the wine will evaporate during cooking), bring to a boil. Reduce the heat to medium-low, cover the stockpot partially with a lid and simmer for 20 minutes. Remove the pot from the heat and let the tomato mixture cool slightly while you prepare the zucchini.

Melt 4 tablespoons of butter in a sauté pan over medium-high heat. Add the diced zucchini and a pinch of salt and cook, stirring occasionally, until the zucchini is crisp-tender but not browned, about 10 minutes. Set aside. Puree the soup in a blender (in batches) with the top vented. Return the soup to the pot, add the cream, and heat through. Stir in the zucchini and serve, garnished with chopped basil. Serves 6.

Nutritional info: Calories: 302; Total Fat: 10g; Protein: 5.7g; Carbohydrates: 55g; Sugars: 16g.

> **TIP** ·····
>
> The whole family will be swept off their feet by the creamy and tangy taste of this real tomato soup. It's equally good served warm with a grilled cheese sandwich, or in hotter months you can serve it well-chilled.

Triple Squash Soup

1 small pie pumpkin (about 3 pounds)
1 acorn squash (about 1 1/2–1 3/4 pounds)
1 butternut squash (about 1 1/2–2 pounds)
2 tablespoon olive oil
1 cup onion, chopped
1 apple, peeled and roughly chopped
2 cloves garlic, minced
1 teaspoon fresh ginger, minced
2 tablespoons honey
2 1/2 teaspoons curry powder
1/4 teaspoon cayenne
1 15-ounce can light coconut milk
4–6 cups vegetable broth
Sea salt to taste

Roast the squash: cut each squash in half, put face down on a cookie sheet, add about 1 cup of water to the pan. Roast in 375°F oven for 40–50 minutes until soft. Cool, remove seeds, scrape flesh from each half of squash into a bowl and set aside. You want to yield about 2 1/2–3 pounds of flesh. (This step can be done up to 3 days in advance.)

> **TIP**
>
> Pumpkin is a member of the squash family, which accounts for the name of this soup. Canned pumpkin can be substituted for fresh, but you'll get a different result because roasting fresh pumpkin deepens the flavor and brings out the sweetness.

Make the soup: heat the olive oil in a large stock pot, sauté the onions until soft. Add the garlic, ginger, curry powder, cayenne and apple, stir well and let cook 2–3 minutes. Add the squash and broth, bring to a boil, reduce heat to a simmer. Add coconut milk, honey, and continue simmering for another 30–45 minutes, until all ingredients are very soft. Purée the soup with a hand-held machine, a blender or food processor. Adjust taste for salt. Serves 6.

Nutritional info: Calories: 302; Total Fat: 10g; Protein: 5.7g; Carbohydrates: 55g; Sugars: 16g.

(N/AL) (C) (MS/DS) (F) (N) (TA)

Red Beans and Rice Soup

1 pound red beans, soaked 8 hours
    or more, rinsed
1/2 pound kielbasa, diced
1 cup onion, chopped
3/4 cup celery, diced
1/2 cup red bell pepper, diced
2–3 cloves garlic, minced
2 teaspoons dark brown sugar
1 1/2 teaspoons dry thyme leaves
2 bay leaves
2 tablespoons apple cider vinegar
6–7 cups chicken broth, preferably
    homemade
2/3 cup Basmati or Thai jasmine rice
Chopped scallions for garnish

Place rinsed beans in a large soup pot and add enough water to cover by 2 inches. Bring the beans to a boil and cover, simmering about 1 hour. Cook until "al dente" or firm to the bite. (You can also reduce the cook time to 15 minutes over a good boil and turn off the heat and let the beans sit for an hour or so in the water.) Drain and discard the liquid.

    Sauté the kielbasa in a large soup pot over medium heat for about 5 minutes; add the onion, celery, bell pepper, garlic and seasonings. Cook, stirring constantly, another 3–4 minutes. Deglaze the pan with vinegar, add broth, beans and rice, and simmer 30–45 minutes until rice is cooked. Adjust taste for salt and pepper, serve garnished with chopped scallions. Serves 6.

Nutritional info: Calories: 399; Total Fat: 14g; Protein: 19.5g; Carbohydrates: 48g; Sugars: 8g.

(N/AL) (C) (MS/DS) (F) (N) (TA)

TIP ·····

The combination of beans, rice and smoky kielbasa is a great source of protein and satisfies carbohydrate cravings, a common side-effect of steroids. This soup is sure to awaken tired taste buds and help fuel a depleted body.

Zesty Summer Watermelon Gazpacho

· ·

3 cups seedless watermelon, cubed
1 English (hothouse style) cucumber, chopped
1 red bell pepper, chopped
1/2 onion, chopped
1/4 jalapeno pepper, finely chopped
2 tablespoons lemon juice
1 tablespoon olive oil
1 tablespoon fresh mint, chopped
1 tablespoon fresh ginger, minced
1 tablespoon honey
1/4 cup pineapple juice
1 tablespoon fresh mint, chopped, for garnish

Working in batches, process the watermelon, the cucumber and red bell pepper separately in a food processor, then combine them in a large bowl or pitcher. Process the onion, jalapeno pepper, ginger and mint together and add to the bowl or pitcher. Lastly add the lemon juice, olive oil, honey and pineapple juice and mix well. The gazpacho should be well blended but retain some texture. Refrigerate a minimum of 1 hour or up to 12 hours. Serve in bowls and garnish with chopped mint. Serves 6.

Nutritional info: Calories 75; Total Fat: 2.5g; Protein: 1g; Carbohydrates: 13g; Sugars: 10.5g.

(N/AL) (C) (MS/DS) (F) (TA)

TIP · · · · ·

Deliciously refreshing and a nice twist on a summer classic! The watermelon helps with hydration, the ginger and mint can ease an upset stomach, and the overall sweetness of this cold soup will appeal to young and old.

Because all the ingredients are consumed uncooked, this soup would not be suitable for a neutropenic diet.

"We are a 'live to eat' family, so food has always been important to me. When food restrictions were placed on my diet because of the cancer treatments, they affected not only me but my family. It would have been helpful to have a single source for food options that I could eat, both in and out of the hospital. This book will be extremely helpful for families who are in need of tasty and nutritious recipes for their children who have special dietary needs and limitations due to chemo-therapy."

— *Bridget, age 19, Hodgkin's Lymphoma, and her mother, Kathy A.*

Chapter 4

We Need a Little Comfort: Dishes for All Moods and Matters

Most of us have a favorite dish or secret family recipe that brings comfort and good memories. Assembled here are some recipes that may have a familiar ring and here's why: kids respond to what they know they like, especially when they aren't feeling well. Some of these recipes will help re-ignite impaired taste buds, and some will help with fatigue. Included are suggestions and substitutions recommended if there are multiple side effects at issue, as well as pointers for a neutropenic diet. Side effects from treatment can affect appetite, taste and most certainly, moods. Having a familiar food that brings comfort and nutrition in one bite can help tame the vampire.

Fabien's Classic Fresh Basil Pesto

1 large bunch fresh basil, rinsed and
    stems removed
1–2 cloves garlic
1/2 cup pine nuts
1/2 cup grated Parmesan cheese
3/4 cup olive oil
Sea salt and lemon juice to taste

Put the basil and garlic in the bowl of a food processor
and process until finely chopped. Add the pine nuts and
Parmesan and process until it forms a paste. With the
motor running, add the olive oil until the paste thins to
desired consistency. Taste and adjust with a little squeeze
of lemon juice and sea salt. Makes 6 servings.

Nutritional info (1 serving): Calories: 353;
Total Fat: 37g; Protein: 5g;
Carbohydrates: 2.4g; Sugars: 0g.

(F) (TA)

Awesome Asparagus Pesto

1 bunch asparagus spears (about 1 pound), trimmed of tough ends
3 cups fresh baby spinach leaves
2 cloves garlic, peeled
1/2 cup grated Parmesan cheese, plus more for topping
3/4 cup pine nuts
1/4 cup extra-virgin olive oil, plus more for topping
2 tablespoons fresh squeezed lemon juice
1/2 teaspoon sea salt
pinch red pepper or to taste (optional)
1/2 pound penne or farfalle (bowtie) pasta

Bring 2 pots of water to a rolling boil, one large for the pasta and one medium for the asparagus. While the water is heating, put the pine nuts in a single layer in a large skillet. Heat on medium heat, stirring occasionally, until fragrant and lightly browned. Remove pine nuts from pan and set aside. You will use 1/2 cup of the pine nuts for the pesto paste and 1/4 cup to mix in whole.

When the water for the asparagus comes to a boil, drop spears in and cook for only 2–3 minutes, until they are bright green and barely tender. Drain under cold water to stop the cooking. Cut the tips off of several spears and set aside for garnish. Put the rest of the asparagus, spinach, garlic, Parmesan and 1/2 cup of the pine nuts into a food processor. Process and, with the motor running, drizzle in the olive oil until a paste forms. If too thick, thin it with a bit of the asparagus or pasta water. Add the lemon juice and sea salt, taste and adjust seasoning.

Cook the pasta according to package directions, or until desired "al dente." Drain and toss immediately with 1 cup of the asparagus pesto. Serve sprinkled with the remaining 1/4 cup toasted pine nuts, the asparagus tips, a dusting of Parmesan, and a light drizzle of olive oil. Serves 6.

Nutritional info: Calories: 299; Total Fat: 23g; Protein: 9.8g; Carbohydrates: 17g; Sugars: 2g.

TIP ·····

Asparagus not only has anti-inflammatory properties, but it is a great source of fiber. Other health benefits include promoting digestive health, and asparagus is a good source of vitamin K, vitamin A, folic acid and B vitamins—which are essential for producing energy. Spinach is an excellent source of iron and can be very beneficial during treatment, since iron is an integral component of hemoglobin. In addition, spinach has at least 13 different flavenoid compounds, which contain impressive anti-cancer properties.

NOTE: If neutropenia is an issue, add the spinach and the garlic to the asparagus and cook both together for 2 minutes. Toasting the pine nuts also eliminates any concern of eating raw foods.

(F) (MS/DS) (N/AL)

Best Italian Meatballs
and Terrific Tomato Sauce

2 pounds organic free-range ground
  turkey (dark meat), or grass-fed
  organic ground beef (90/10)
1 cup Panko breadcrumbs (or
  unseasoned regular breadcrumbs)
3/4 cup Romano or Parmesan cheese,
  grated
1/2 cup whole milk
1/2 cup low-sodium beef broth
  plus 1 cup for cooking (can
  substitute chicken broth)
3 eggs, lightly beaten
1/2 cup fresh parsley, chopped
2 tablespoons dried oregano
1 tablespoon garlic, minced
2 teaspoons dried basil
1 teaspoon crushed red
  pepper flakes (optional)

Combine the ground turkey (or beef) and the Panko; mix
well with a fork. Whisk together the remaining ingredients,
add the mixture to the meat. Mix well. Refrigerate at least
30 minutes, or until ready to use. Shape the meatballs about
2 inches in diameter. Arrange them in a shallow pan, cover
the bottom of the pan with 1 cup additional broth. Bake 25
minutes at 375°F. Makes about 30 (1 1/2 ounce) meatballs.
Serves 8.

Nutritional info: Calories: 264; Total Fat: 14g; Protein: 29.5g;
Carbohydrates: 5.5g; Sugars: 1g

FOR TERRIFIC TOMATO SAUCE:

1 1/2 cups sweet onion, chopped
1/4 cup olive oil
2 1/2 pounds fresh tomatoes, chopped, or 3 (14-ounce)
    cans diced tomatoes
1/2 cup reserved meatball pan drippings (recipe at left)
1/2 cup fresh parsley, minced
1 tablespoon agave nectar
1 teaspoon crushed red pepper flakes (optional)
Sea salt, to taste

In a medium sauté pan, heat the olive oil over medium-high
heat. Add the onions and sauté until translucent, about 5
minutes. Add garlic, cook another minute (or until you begin
to smell it), then add the tomatoes, pan drippings, parsley,
agave nectar and pepper flakes. Simmer 20–30 minutes.
Add cooked meatballs, simmer another 5–10 minutes to heat
through the meatballs. Serve over cooked pasta. Serves 4.

Nutritional info: Calories: 103; Total Fat: 7g; Protein: 2g;
Carbohydrates: 9.5g; Sugars: 5.5g.

(F) (N) (TA)

TIP 1 ·······

Ground turkey or ground
beef? While both are an
excellent source of protein,
the ground turkey will be
more easily digested, which
may be an appropriate choice
if the patient needs to ease
back into solid foods. Ground
beef is an excellent choice for
countering fatigue and the
side effects of steroids.

TIP 2 ·······

You can cook these meatballs
ahead and then freeze them,
or roll them into desired size
and freeze them uncooked.
This works especially well for
soups—simply drop the
uncooked frozen meatballs
directly into your simmering
soup. Try adding them to the
Kid's Favorite Chicken Noodle
Soup (pg. 27) for another
boost of protein.

Turkey Burgers with Oven-Roasted Sweet Potato Fries

1 1/2 pounds organic free-range ground
    turkey (combination of white and
    dark meat)
1 clove garlic, minced
1 tablespoon grated sweet onion
2 teaspoons Dijon mustard
1 teaspoon reduced-sodium Tamari
    or soy sauce

4 large whole wheat buns
Tomato slices, lettuce, sliced cheddar or
    goat cheese—garnish (optional)

(F) (N)

TIP

Zing up the burgers with Lemon-Honey
Mustard: to 1/4 cup Dijon mustard,
add 1 heaping tablespoon clover
honey, 1/2 teaspoon lemon zest and
1 teaspoon fresh lemon juice. Mix
together and let sit while you prepare
the burgers. The lemon, mustard and
honey combination can really wake up
impaired taste buds!

Put the turkey, garlic, grated onion, mustard and
Tamari sauce in a large mixing bowl and mix well
with a wooden spoon. Preheat the grill or griddle
to medium-high. Divide the turkey into 4 equal
portions and form the meat into burgers. Grill until
cooked through, about 3-4 minutes on each side. If
using cheese, add during the last 2 minutes of cooking. Put the burgers on the buns, garnish with tomato
and lettuce if desired. (Omit the lettuce and tomato
if neutropenia is an issue). Serves 4.

Nutritional info: Calories: 479; Total Fat: 22g;
Protein: 48g; Carbohydrates: 24g; Sugars: 4.6g.

OVEN-ROASTED SWEET POTATO FRIES

1 1/2 pounds organic sweet potatoes (garnet or jewel)
1/4 cup olive oil
1 teaspoon sea salt
1/2 teaspoon paprika
1/4 teaspoon cinnamon

Preheat oven to 425°F. Line a baking sheet with aluminum foil. Peel the sweet potatoes and cut into 1/2 inch strips. Transfer potatoes to a resealable plastic bag or a low glass dish, add the oil, sea salt, paprika and cinnamon. Close the bag and toss well to coat the fries. Spread the potatoes on the baking sheet, making sure they don't crowd each other. Cook for 30 minutes, without turning them, then give the baking sheet a good shake so the potatoes turn on their own. If they don't, let them cook another 5–10 minutes and try again. Continue to cook for a total for about 45 minutes, until they are lightly browned. Let cool slightly before serving. Serves 4.

Nutritional info: Calories: 182; Total Fat: 9g; Protein: 2.3g; Carbohydrates: 23.7g; Sugars: 7.3g.

(F) (N) (C) (MS/DS)

TIP ·····

If you love the sweet potato fries idea, try them with a little grated Parmesan and Italian herbs, or add a dash of cayenne pepper. A more complex flavor can help stimulate an appetite.

Baked Salmon with Delightful Dill-Yogurt Sauce

4 4-ounce wild-caught salmon fillets
1 tablespoon fresh squeezed lemon juice
1/2 teaspoon sea salt

FOR THE SAUCE:

1 cup fresh dill, finely chopped (or
   1 tablespoon dried)
1 1/2 cups plain yogurt, whole milk
   or low fat
1 teaspoon fresh squeezed lemon juice
1 teaspoon sea salt

Preheat the oven to 350°F. Arrange the salmon fillets in a glass baking dish, sprinkle generously with lemon juice and a touch of sea salt. Bake for 12–15 minutes, until the fish is opaque and flakes easily.

While the fish is cooking, make the sauce. Put the dill in the bowl of a food processor, and process until finely chopped. Add 1/2 cup of yogurt and process well again, until the sauce becomes quite green and somewhat runny. Add the remaining 1 cup of yogurt, the lemon juice and the salt. Pulse briefly 2–3 times but don't over-mix or the yogurt will become too runny. Taste and adjust for salt. Serves 4.

TIP ······

Yogurt is an excellent source of lactobacillus, a very beneficial bacteria which helps restore health to the gastrointestinal tract, helps fight intestinal infections and keeps the immune system strong.

VARIATION: Salmon is also wonderful poached. In a straight-sided sauté pan, bring 1 cup of vegetable broth to a simmer over medium heat. Add the fillets, cover with the lid ajar, and poach for 7–9 minutes. Remove the salmon carefully with a spatula.

Nutritional info: Calories: 252; Total Fat: 9.6g; Protein: 32g; Carbohydrates: 7g; Sugars: 6.7g.

(F) (N) (MS/DS)

"Healthy eating is a lesson for the family and that is what this book teaches. Ashley loves vegetables, fruits and salads and yet we were both a little skeptical of some of the recipes until we tasted them. The smoothies, the soups are all delicious. I've brought it home to the family and we are now making better food choices. I think that is so encouraging to kids and their parents."

— *Jeanette G, grandmother, and Ashley, age 15, Hodgkin's Lymphoma*

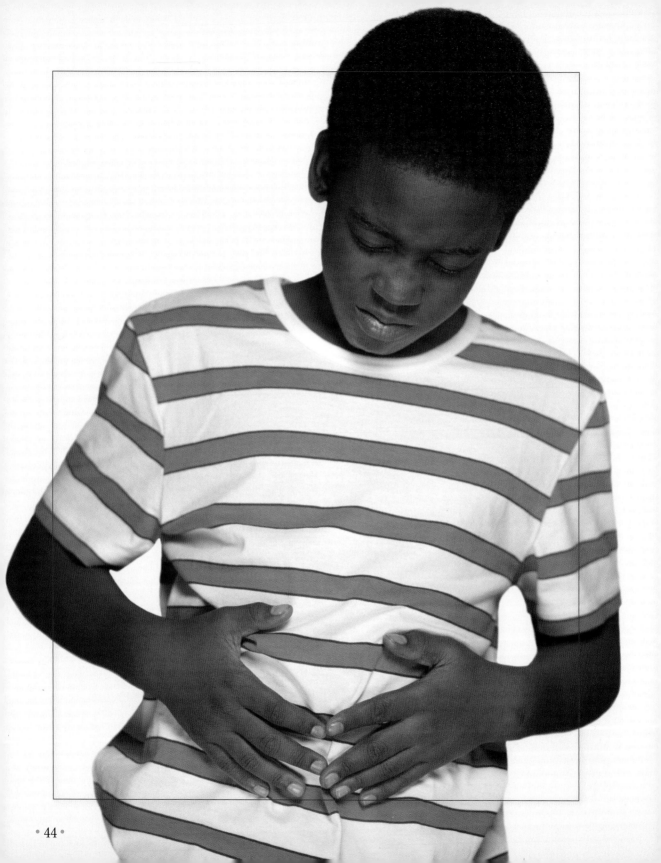

Chapter 5

Digestion: Easy-to-Eat Sides

Children seem to naturally gravitate to "white" foods, like rice, potatoes and bread. Rice and potatoes digest easily and the mild taste of certain foods is easy on developing taste buds. Use these mild-tasting foods as a means to add nutrition. A baked potato is entirely healthy on its own, and adding toppings from fresh, wholesome and organic sources makes it even better. Substituting an authentic rice variety for a box of converted rice (which has been stripped of nutrients) is also a great idea. There is a definite place for "white" foods, especially as building blocks to carry a nutritious wallop.

Let's Talk Rice!

Rice and grains, some of the world's oldest foods, have been used in many cultures for thousands of years. The varieties of rice are countless—from common short grain, medium grain, long grain white and brown rice to Italy's favored Arborio risotto rice, fragrant Thai jasmine rice, Japanese sweet rice, Basmati rice and an African favorite, broken rice (which is in fact the bits that are left after rice is sorted). The colors are endless— from white rice, brown rice, wild rice, red Bhutanese rice and even Forbidden Black rice, which long ago was reserved for the emperors of China. Wild rice is not technically a rice, but rather the seed of an aquatic grass found around lake areas, but it is now cultivated as a rice. White rice is stripped of its hull, bran and germ, which is why the nutritional value is not as high as brown or dark rice. Darker rice has a nuttier flavor, takes much longer to cook and generally is more nutritious, but sometimes the light texture of white rice is appropriate for digestive needs and preparation time. The fragrant smell and flavor of Basmati and Thai jasmine rice make these a great place to start experimenting with new kinds of rice. Eventually it would be nutritionally beneficial to discover some of the captivating brown, red and black rice varieties.

Basic Steamed Rice

• •

2 cups Basmati or Thai jasmine rice
4 cups vegetable or low-sodium chicken
   broth (can substitute water)
1/2 teaspoon sea salt

Rinse the rice well in a colander under cool water, then transfer to a medium-sized saucepan and add the broth or water and salt. Cover and bring to a low boil over medium heat, lower the heat and simmer on very low heat until the water has been absorbed, 15–20 minutes. Let rice sit off the heat for 5 minutes before serving. Serves 6.

Nutritional info: Calories: 177; Total Fat: 1.3g; Protein: 3.6g; Carbohydrates: 37g; Sugars: 1.4g.

(N/AL) (MS/DS) (F) (N) (TA)

Destiny, 16 months, Infantile Fibromatosis

FRIED RICE: A great way to use cooked rice is turning it into a variation of fried rice. In a sauté pan, melt 1 tablespoon of butter, add 1/2 cup each chopped onion, diced carrots, frozen peas and corn. Cover and cook over low heat about 5 minutes. Add 1 1/2 cups cooked rice and a tablespoon of water or broth to prevent the rice from sticking. In a small bowl, crack an egg and scramble. Push all of the rice to one side of the pan, clearing enough space to add the scrambled egg. Cook the egg, and gently fold into the rice and vegetables. Makes a nutritious snack, light meal or breakfast.

RICE PILAF: Rice pilaf is an easy way to enhance cooked rice. In a sauté pan, heat 1 tablespoon of olive oil, add 1/2 small onion, finely chopped, 1 clove garlic, minced, and 1/4 cup chopped pecans OR pine nuts. Cook a few minutes until the garlic is fragrant and the nuts are lightly browned. Add 1 1/2 cups cooked rice and 1 tablespoon water or broth to prevent the rice from sticking. Adjust for salt and serve.

COCONUT RICE: Substituting light coconut milk for part of the liquid will lend itself to a more fragrant outcome. For example, use 1 cup rice to 1 cup coconut milk and 1 cup water and follow the same cooking directions. Most rice-to-liquid ratios will be 2 parts liquid to 1 part rice. Some long-grain rice, especially brown, will need slightly more liquid.

Let's Talk Potatoes!

Widely available and inexpensive, potatoes are the number one crop not only in the United States but also around the world. Properly prepared, they can be nutritious and satisfying, and their neutral starchy flavor is a good accompaniment to many other foods. Potatoes are a concentrated source of vitamin B6, vitamin C, fiber, potassium and other minerals. Healthy steamed potatoes deliver the best source of nutrients, slow-baked potatoes will deliver a richer flavor. Since most of the nutrients are just under the skin, it is best to avoid peeling them. While the skin by itself is full of fiber, the potato contains chlorogenic acid, a chemical that has been found to prevent certain cell mutations leading to cancer. There are over 100 varieties globally, but the most familiar to Americans include Idaho's russet potatoes, Yukon or gold, red bliss, new or baby potatoes and blue-fleshed potatoes. Buying organic potatoes is a good choice, since most commercial potatoes have been treated with pesticides including sprout inhibitors that can cause allergic reactions.

Oven-Roasted Potatoes

2 pounds Yukon gold, red bliss or new "baby" potatoes, or a combination, unpeeled
1/4 cup olive oil
1 teaspoon sea salt

Heat oven to 425°F. Toss the potatoes with olive oil and salt. Spread on a baking sheet and roast for 15 minutes. Toss and roast another 15 minutes, or until nicely browned and tender when pierced with a fork. Serves 6–8.

Nutritional info: Calories: 160; Total Fat: 6.9g; Protein: 2.6g; Carbohydrates: 22g; Sugars: 1.6g.

VARIATION: Sometimes a little herbed flavoring is called for, in which case you can sprinkle 1/2–1 teaspoon each chopped rosemary and thyme just before you pop them in the oven.

(N/AL) (MS/DS) (F) (N) (TA)

Warm Roasted Potato Salad
with Black Olive and Mint Pesto

2 pounds Yukon gold, red bliss or new "baby" potatoes, or a combination, unpeeled
1/4 cup olive oil
1/2 cup (2 ounces) feta cheese, crumbled
3–4 scallions, trimmed and sliced, for garnish
Chopped mint, for garnish

Heat oven to 425°F. Toss the potatoes with olive oil. Spread on a baking sheet and roast for 15 minutes. Toss and roast another 15 minutes, or until nicely browned and tender when pierced with a fork. While the potatoes are still hot, toss with pesto. Garnish with scallions and chopped mint. Serve warm or at room temperature. Serves 6–8.

PESTO:

3/4 cup pitted black olives (Kalamata
  or oil-cured Moroccan)
1/4 cup olive oil
2 tablespoons lightly packed chopped
  fresh mint
1 small shallot, minced
1 tablespoon fresh lemon juice, more
  to taste
Salt and pepper to taste

Put all ingredients in a food processor.
Process, stopping to scrape the sides of
the bowl with a rubber spatula as needed,
until mixture is smooth. Adjust the taste
with salt and pepper and lemon, as needed.
Serves 6.

Nutritional info (1 serving): Calories: 355;
Total Fat: 22.5g; Protein: 9g; Carbohydrates:
34.7g; Sugars: 2.5g.

(N/AL) (MS/DS) (F) (N) (TA)

TIP

So you're thinking, "There's no way
my child would go for this and even
I don't like olives," right? This was
a hugely popular dish with the kids
and adults, despite any perceived
skepticism. Maybe it was because
the kids weren't really aware of the
ingredients in this, or perhaps it was
the salty combination of olives and
feta that satisfied the salt cravings of
some of the patients. Whatever it was,
the flavor made it a home run. If
neutropenia is an issue, lightly sauté
the shallots in olive oil before putting
them in the pesto, omit the scallion
garnish and substitute dried mint
for fresh.

Fluffy Mashed Potatoes with Perfect Poached Eggs

2 Idaho russet potatoes (can substitute
    one sweet potato and one russet),
    peeled and cut into chunks
2 tablespoons unsalted butter
1 tablespoon sour cream
1/2 teaspoon sea salt

2 eggs, poached in simmering water with 1 tablespoon white vinegar (directions below)

Put the potato chunks in a pot and cover with cold water. Bring to a boil, reduce the heat and cook until very tender when pierced with a fork, about 10 minutes. Drain well, transfer back to the pot, and with an electric beater whip the potatoes until fluffy, about 1 minute. Add the butter, sour cream and salt; whip another minute. Adjust for taste. Keep warm while you poach the eggs.

TIP ·····

This old European dish was commonly used as comfort food for rebuilding strength and appetite after illness. The potassium in the potatoes and the protein in the eggs are beneficial for battling nausea, diarrhea and fatigue.

To poach eggs, bring a saucepan filled about 2/3 full of water—enough to cover the eggs—to a boil. Reduce heat to a simmer. Add the vinegar to the simmering water (this will help the egg coagulate). Crack one egg into a ramekin or small bowl and carefully slide the egg into the water. Do the same for the second egg. Cook for 3–4 minutes, making sure the water does not return to a boil. Remove with a slotted spoon, letting excess water drip into the pan. Serve on top of mashed potatoes. Serves 2.

Nutritional info: Calories: 331; Total Fat: 18g; Protein: 9.5g; Carbohydrates: 34g; Sugars: 1.6g.

(N/AL) (C) (MS/DS) (F) (N) (TA)

Simply Sweet Potatoes with Creamy Miso Dressing

2 pounds sweet potatoes, peeled and cut into chunks
2 tablespoons white miso* paste
2 teaspoons honey
2 tablespoons mirin* wine (can substitute sake or
    white wine, add 1 teaspoon agave nectar)
1 tablespoon white vinegar
1/2 teaspoon dark toasted sesame oil

Put the sweet potato chunks in a pot and cover with cold water.
Bring to a boil, reduce heat and cook until tender when pierced
with a fork, about 10–15 minutes. While the potatoes are cooking,
whisk together the remaining ingredients for the dressing. Drain
the potatoes, transfer to a serving bowl and toss with dressing.
Serve warm, at room temperature or chilled. Serves 4.

Nutritional info: Calories: 216; Total Fat: 1.4g; Protein: 4g;
Carbohydrates: 47g; Sugars: 17.5g.

*available at
Asian grocery stores*

(N/AL) (C) (MS/DS) (F) (N) (TA)

"Open Sesame" Noodles

6 tablespoons reduced sodium soy sauce or
  Tamari sauce
5 tablespoons dark toasted sesame oil
3 tablespoons balsamic vinegar
1 tablespoon agave nectar or natural sugar,
  preferably maple sugar or evaporated cane sugar
1 teaspoon sea salt
1/2 teaspoon hot chili oil (optional)

1 bunch scallions, finely sliced
1/4 cup cilantro, chopped

1 16-ounce box angel hair pasta

Stir together the first six ingredients for the noodle dressing and set aside. Slice the scallions and chop the cilantro, reserve for garnish. Cook the pasta according to box directions. As soon as the pasta is drained, transfer to a large bowl and add the sesame dressing. Using tongs, stir well, making sure the noodles are evenly coated with the dressing. Let sit for at least 30 minutes and up to several hours before serving. Stir occasionally, making sure all the dressing gets soaked up. Stir in the scallions and cilantro before serving. Serve at room temperature or chilled. Serves 6.

Nutritional info: Calories: 330; Total Fat: 12g;
Protein: 10.6g; Carbohydrates: 48.6g; Sugars: 3.8g.

(F) (N) (TA)

TIP ·····

These noodles are an excellent accompaniment to the Baked Salmon with Delightful Dill-Yogurt Sauce (pg. 42). They keep well for several days refrigerated, and make an excellent snack or school lunch and will satisfy carbohydrate cravings. If neutropenia is an issue, simply omit the scallions and cilantro.

"Destinee isn't an adventurous eater but assisting Danielle during the cooking demonstrations in the clinic has made her want to try new, healthy things—and she finds she likes them. She has really enjoyed the cooking demonstrations during the long clinic visits."

— *Lemeisha S, mother, and Destinee, age 6, Leukemia (T-cell ALL)*

Chapter 6

Vibrant and Vital Veggies

Taking a kid to a farmers' market turns the day into an adventure for both child and those around him or her. The fresh air, the colors of all the fruits and vegetables—pretty soon a young forager will be loading up a parent's basket with more apples, carrots, beets and eggplant than the family could possibly eat in a week. During treatment, it's so vitally important to eat a rainbow of vegetables, because the nutrients are crucial to good health and the phytochemicals packed into these gems will help combat future illness, including cancers. With so many quick and easy ways of making vegetables and so many choices, it's easy to find a few to really love. Here is a small sampling of some easy, reliable and deliciously approved recipes.

Butternut Squash with Ginger-Garlic Sauté

1 (1–1 1/2 pounds) butternut squash, peeled,
   seeds removed and cut into chunks
1 tablespoon fresh ginger, minced
2 cloves garlic, minced
1 tablespoon butter
1 teaspoon sea salt
1/4 teaspoon white pepper (optional)
2 tablespoons fresh parsley, chopped,
   for garnish (optional)

In a sauté pan large enough to hold all the squash without overly crowding, bring 1 cup of water to a boil over medium-high heat. Add the squash, reduce the heat to medium-low and cover. Simmer 3 minutes, uncover and add the minced garlic and ginger. Add a scant amount of water if it all has been absorbed, taking care not to overdo it by immersing the squash completely in water. Cover and cook another 5 minutes until tender when pierced with a knife. Add the butter, salt and pepper and stir gently. Garnish with parsley. Serves 6.

Nutritional info: Calories: 51.5; Total Fat: 2.2g; Protein: 1g; Carbohydrates: 8g; Sugars: 2.8g.

(N/AL) (C) (F) (N) (TA)

TIP

If you've never wrestled with a whole butternut squash, it can be a little intimidating at first. A good chef's knife or a strong peeler goes a long way. Cut the squash in half, at the narrow part of the neck, so you have two pieces, one very rounded and one narrow. Place the cut side down flat on the cutting board and carefully cut or peel away the thick outer layer. Start at the top and cut or peel from top to bottom. If you decide to save the peeling experience for another time, most grocery stores carry precut squash.

Perfect Green Beans

1 pound fresh green beans
1 tablespoon fresh squeezed lemon juice
2 tablespoons olive oil
Zest from 1 lemon
1 teaspoon sea salt

Take a handful of green beans and tap the ends on a cutting board to even them out. Cut the ends of a handful of beans all at once. Turn the beans around and do the same to other the end of the beans. Fill a 6-quart pot or a large deep sauté pan half-full of water and bring to a boil. Drop the green beans in and cook for 8 minutes (7 minutes if you like them crunchy). Drain and rinse immediately with cold water to stop the cooking. In a small bowl, mix together the lemon juice, lemon zest, salt and olive oil. Just before serving, toss the green beans with the dressing. Serves 4.

Nutritional info: Calories: 120; Total Fat: 9.5g; Protein: 2g; Carbohydrates: 8.8g; Sugars: 1.7g.

(C) (F) (N) (TA)

TIP .... What makes these perfect? Green beans are so often overcooked, which depletes the nutritional value, not to mention taste and color. This method cooks the beans "al dente," tender outside, slightly firm inside. They are equally wonderful served warm with a pat of butter and a dash of sea salt.

Sophie, age 7, Neuroblastoma

TIP ·····

With over 100 varieties and colors that range from white, red, yellow, orange and purple, we have learned from Bugs Bunny that carrots are good at any time. Improperly stored, carrots can lose flavor and up to 30% of their vitamins, so using fresh, whole carrots will give you maximum flavor and nutrition. The bagged "baby" carrots found in most supermarkets are actually pieces of regular carrots shaped to be miniature.

(N/AL) (C) (F) (TA)

Shredded Lemony Carrot Salad

· ·

4 cups shredded carrots (about 4–6 medium carrots, scrubbed,
    ends removed and shredded)
1/4 cup fresh squeezed lemon juice
1/4 cup olive oil
1 teaspoon sea salt
2 tablespoons fresh dill, chopped or 2 teaspoons dried (optional)

Shred the washed carrots in a food processor or on a grater, transfer to a serving bowl. Mix the lemon juice, olive oil and sea salt in a small bowl. Toss on the carrots and mix well. Add the dill, adjust for salt. Let carrots marinate in the refrigerator for 30 minutes or up to several hours before serving. Serves 4.

Nutritional info: Calories: 174; Total Fat: 14g; Protein: 1g;
Carbohydrates: 12g; Sugars: 5.5g

Zucchini "a la Crème"

1 pound (about 4) zucchini, or a combination of zucchini
    and yellow squash, cut into thin rounds
1 tablespoon olive oil
1 tablespoon butter
1 medium shallot, sliced
1/4 cup heavy cream
1 teaspoon sea salt
1 tablespoon fresh parsley, chopped, for garnish (optional)

Melt the butter in the olive oil in a large sauté pan over
medium heat. Add the shallots and cook a few minutes, until
they become soft and fragrant. Add the sliced zucchini and
salt, cover to allow the squash to sweat and cook until crisp-
tender, about 5 minutes. Just before serving, add the cream
and stir well. Adjust taste for salt. Serves 4.

Nutritional info: Calories: 132; Total Fat: 12g; Protein: 1.4g;
Carbohydrates: 5.7g; Sugars: 2.9g.

(C) (MS/DS) (F) (N)

TIP ·····

An excellent source of
vitamin C and mild in flavor,
summer squash, with its
many varieties and varying
hues of yellows and greens,
is used in everything from
salad to soups and breads.
Keeping it simple sometimes
is the best way to go, and
adding a creamy finish is a
pleasing way to get vitamins
and nutrients into the
patient.

Beet, Tomato and Watermelon Salad with Caramelized Almonds*

2 cups tomatoes, cubed (or cherry tomatoes, halved)
2 cups watermelon, cubed
3 medium-small beets, boiled, peeled and cubed
1 cups slivered almonds
2 tablespoons maple syrup
2 tablespoons natural sugar, preferably maple sugar
   or evaporated cane sugar
2 tablespoons fresh mint, chopped, for garnish

FOR THE DRESSING:

1/4 cup white balsamic
   vinegar (can substitute
   apple cider vinegar)
2 tablespoons olive oil
1 teaspoon sea salt

To cook the beets: place the unpeeled beets in a medium saucepan, and cover them with water. Bring to a boil, reduce heat and simmer until fully cooked, about 45 minutes, or until a knife inserted indicates they are tender. Drain and cool.

Preheat the oven or toaster oven to 350°F. In a small bowl, toss the almonds with the maple syrup and sugar. Spread them evenly on a foil-covered baking sheet and bake until caramelized, 10–20 minutes. Set aside to cool. Break up the clumps into small pieces.

Remove skins from the beets with a peeler or a knife, cut into large dice (cubes), place them in a salad bowl. Cube the tomatoes and watermelon, add them to the beets. Whisk together the vinegar, salt and olive oil, toss into the salad. Serve the salad sprinkled with almonds and garnished with chopped mint. Serves 8.

NOTE: The salad can be prepared ahead of time and kept refrigerated in an airtight container. The beets cooked and unpeeled will keep in the refrigerator for up to 3 days. Add the dressing at the last minute, or it will cause the salad to marinate too much.

Nutritional info: Calories: 260; Total Fat: 17.4g; Protein: 6.3g; Carbohydrates: 23g; Sugars: 14.5g.

(C) (F) (TA)

*Adapted from Myra Kornfeld, **The Healthy Hedonist: More than 200 Delectable Flexitarian Recipes for Relaxed Daily Feasts**, Simon and Schuster Publishers.*

"Food during treatment keeps me distracted and makes me feel happier and loved—especially when it is cooked by Mom. I am not always sure what I want to eat when I am hungry; Danielle's recipes have great variety and allow me to try new things. Mom loves the recipes too because they are healthy and yummy, and take care of the thinking part."

— *Zoe, age 13, Leukemia (Pre-B cell ALL), and her mother, Carmen C.*

Ayden, age 5, Leukemia (Pre-B cell ALL) and little brother Evan

Chapter 7

Satisfying Sweets and Desserts

If you began perusing this book with this chapter, you know the value of eating dessert first, because you just never know what life is going to hand you. Kids are drawn to sweets and a child fighting cancer is no different. All the recipes here have been created with optimal nutrition without giving up the sweet, and you'll be amazed how good they are. Can you imagine a real-tasting chocolate chip cookie made with NO sugar (the chocolate chips are grain-sweetened) and NO white flour? It's here, and it's passed the kid test with flying colors. Healthy doesn't mean tasteless—it means smart choices, a little creativity and an appetite for life.

Chocolate Chip Cookies

6 tablespoons unsalted butter
1/2 cup light agave nectar
1 large egg
1 tablespoon vanilla extract
3/4 cup oat flour
3/4 cup barley flour
1/2 teaspoon baking soda
1/2 teaspoon sea salt
1/2 teaspoon cinnamon
1 cup chocolate chips
   (grain-sweetened preferred)
1 cup pecans, chopped

(F) (N) (TA)

Preheat the oven to 325°F. Prepare 2 baking sheets with spray oil or line with parchment paper.

In a mixing bowl, beat the butter with an electric mixer until creamy. Add the agave nectar and beat until light and fluffy, then add the egg and vanilla. Beat until well mixed, 1–2 minutes.

In a separate bowl, mix together all the dried ingredients. Fold into the butter mixture and combine well, then add the chocolate chips and pecans. Drop by tablespoons onto prepared cookie sheets. Press down the dough slightly to achieve uniform cookie size. Bake for 12–15 minutes (12 minutes for chewy cookies), let cool a few minutes on the cookie sheet then transfer to a rack to cool completely. Makes 2 dozen cookies.

Nutritional info (per cookie):
Calories: 299; Total Fat: 18g;
Protein: 4.4g; Carbohydrates:
33g; Sugars: 16.4g.

Simone, age 9, Brain Tumor
(pilocytic astrocytoma)

Raspberry Nectarine Pecan Crumble

1/2 cup pecans, chopped
1 cup rolled oats
1/2–3/4 cup honey
1/4 cup safflower oil
4 cups raspberries
   (unsweetened, frozen are fine)
2 cups unpeeled nectarines, cut
   into chunks (frozen are fine)

1 cup silken tofu
1/4 cup agave nectar
1 tablespoon vanilla extract

TIP ·····

Team up super-healthy whole grains and juicy fruit, toss in a handful of pecans, and you've got yourself a nutritious dessert you can use as a breakfast too. Try combining strawberries and blueberries, peaches and berries, or apples, pears and figs.

Preheat the oven or toaster oven to 375°F. Put the pecans on a cookie sheet or toaster oven pan and toast for 8–10 minutes, until brown. Cool pecans and add to uncooked rolled oats. Whisk together the honey and the oil in a small bowl, add to the oats and pecans.

Lower the oven temperature to 350°F. Lightly oil a medium glass casserole pan, and layer with raspberries and nectarines. Top with the oats-pecan mixture and bake 20 minutes, or until the fruit is soft and the topping is golden.

While the crumble is baking, puree the tofu with the vanilla and agave until very smooth. Adjust taste to desired sweetness, adding a squeeze of lemon juice if needed. Drizzle the tofu-vanilla cream over the crunch and serve warm. Serves 8.

Nutritional info: Calories: 338; Total Fat: 14.2g; Protein: 5.4g; Carbohydrates: 51.7g; Sugars: 32.6g.

(C) (F) (N) (TA)

Hazelnut Chocolate Chip Brownies*

2 eggs
1 cup apple or pear juice
1/4 cup melted extra-virgin coconut
    oil or butter
1/2 cup maple syrup
1 teaspoon vanilla extract
3/4 cup finely ground raw hazelnuts
    (skins on) or hazelnut flour
1/3 cup brown rice flour
1/4 cup coconut flour
1/2 cup cocoa powder
1 teaspoon baking powder
1/2 teaspoon sea salt
3/4 cup dark chocolate chips

Prcheat the oven to 350. Lightly oil a 9-inch square glass or standard loaf pan.

Whisk the eggs in a large bowl. Add the juice, melted coconut oil, maple syrup and vanilla. In a separate bowl, combine the dry ingredients. Mix well, add to the egg mixture and lastly, add the chocolate chips. Bake 25–30 minutes, or until a toothpick inserted in the center comes out clean (or with only melted chocolate on it). Cool at least 30 minutes before serving. Makes 12 brownies.

TIP ·····

To avoid all sugar, you can replace the dark chocolate chips with grain-sweetened chocolate chips, but the brownies will no longer be gluten-free. We think it's one of the best brownie recipes around—gluten-free or otherwise.

Nutritional info: Calories: 216; Total Fat: 13.5g; Protein: 3.2g; Carbohydrates: 25g; Sugars: 16.5g.

(C) (F) (N) (TA)

*Reprinted with permission: ***Gluten-Free Recipes for the Conscious Cook,*** New Harbinger Publications, Inc. copyright © 2010 Leslie Cerier.

Very Berry Sauce

2 cups berries—combination of strawberries,
    raspberries and blackberries is best
1/2 cup apple or pear juice
1/4 cup agave nectar
1 tablespoon arrowroot dissolved in 1/4 cup cold water

Puree the berries with the juice in a food processor, and if you
wish, strain through a fine-meshed sieve to remove the seeds.
Transfer to a saucepan and add the agave nectar. Bring the
fruit to a low simmer over medium heat until, then add the
arrowroot slurry and stir continuously until the sauce changes
from cloudy to clear and you can feel it thicken. Remove from
heat (it will only take a few minutes) before you see it begin to
boil or the thickener will separate. Cool before using, or serve
warm over ice cream or Comforting Rice Pudding (pg. 71).
Serves 6.

Nutritional info: Calories: 66; Total Fat: 0g; Protein: 0g;
Carbohydrates: 16.5g; Sugars: 13g.

(C) (F) (N) (TA)

TIP 1

Berries, packed with healthy
flavenoids, are a veritable
powerhouse of antioxidants.
And they're so easy to love!
Kids never seem to get enough
of them, so when the appetite is
there, hand them fresh fruits and
berries. This cooked sauce is a
great substitute for fresh berries,
especially when the patient is
neutropenic. Try it on pancakes
too!

TIP 2

Arrowroot is a healthy substitute
for cornstarch and works extremely well as a thickener in
puddings, pies and sauces. It
must be dissolved in cold liquid
before it's added to a pot or you
will get lumps, but it can also
separate if you over-boil it in
the fruit. It gives the fruit a lovely
shine, which is one reason it's
so popular for pies.

Pumpkin Molasses Pie

1 9-inch store-bought deep dish pie crust,
    made with organic flour or gluten-free

1 small pie pumpkin (about 3 pounds) or
    can substitute 3 cups canned pumpkin
4 eggs, lightly beaten
1/2 cup honey
1/4 cup dark molasses
1 cup half and half
1 teaspoon pumpkin pie spice (or
    substitute 1/2 teaspoon ground
    ginger and 1/2 teaspoon cinnamon)
1 teaspoon sea salt

TIP ·····

Pumpkins get their deep color from beta-carotene, an immune enhancer also found in carrots, melons, winter squash and mangoes, as well as many other fruits and vegetables. They are also rich in carotenoids, which research has shown helps prevent cancers, heart disease and even the common cold! Pumpkin seeds are an excellent source of zinc, a mineral crucial for a healthy immune system.

Cook the pumpkin: cut in half, cut side down on a cookie sheet or glass baking pan, add 1/2 inch of water. Bake in 350°F oven for 40–50 minutes, until soft when pierced with a knife. Cool, remove seeds, scrape flesh from the inside, and puree until smooth in a food processor or blender. Yield should be 3 cups or more. (This step can be done up to 3 days in advance; pureed pumpkin also freezes very well.)

Preheat the oven to 350°F. Combine the eggs, honey, molasses, half and half and seasonings and mix well. Add 3 cups of pureed pumpkin, mix well and pour into prepared pie crust. Bake 50 minutes, or until custard is firm and top is a glossy deep brown. Cool completely before serving. Serves 6.

Nutritional info: Calories: 220; Total Fat: 8g; Protein: 4g; Carbohydrates: 34.8g; Sugars: 23.4g.

(N/AL) (C) (MS/DS) (F) (N) (TA)

Comforting Rice Pudding

1/2 cup golden raisins (optional)
1 cup boiling water
1/3 cup slivered almonds (optional)
3 1/2 cups cooked medium- or long-grain
 rice, at room temperature (Arborio
 rice preferred)
2 1/2 cups milk
2 1/2 cups heavy cream
2/3 cup light agave nectar
1 1/4 teaspoons pure vanilla extract
1 teaspoon ground cinnamon

Place the raisins in a bowl and cover with the water. Let sit until plumped, 5 minutes. Drain.

In a skillet over medium heat, toast the almonds until golden and fragrant, 3–5 minutes. Remove from the heat.

In a large saucepan, combine the rice, milk, cream, agave nectar and salt. Bring to a simmer, stirring, over medium heat. Reduce the heat slightly to maintain a low simmer and cook uncovered, stirring frequently, until the mixture starts to thicken, about 30 minutes. Continue to cook, stirring occasionally to prevent the rice from sticking, until a spoon is just able to stand up in the pudding, about 5 minutes. Remove from heat and stir in the raisins, almonds, and remaining ingredients. Serves 6.

Nutritional info: Calories: 429; Total Fat: 27g; Protein: 6.2g; Carbohydrates: 42g; Sugars: 21g.

(N/AL) (MS/DS) (F) (N)

Citus and Pomegranate Terrine

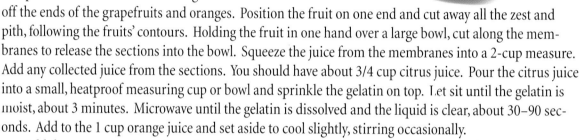

4 grapefruits
4 large navel oranges
2 envelopes unflavored gelatin
    powder
1 cup orange juice
1/4 cup fresh pomegranate seeds
Agave nectar to taste

Have ready a 9 x 5-inch Pyrex or ceramic loaf pan and make room in the fridge. Cut off the ends of the grapefruits and oranges. Position the fruit on one end and cut away all the zest and pith, following the fruits' contours. Holding the fruit in one hand over a large bowl, cut along the membranes to release the sections into the bowl. Squeeze the juice from the membranes into a 2-cup measure. Add any collected juice from the sections. You should have about 3/4 cup citrus juice. Pour the citrus juice into a small, heatproof measuring cup or bowl and sprinkle the gelatin on top. Let sit until the gelatin is moist, about 3 minutes. Microwave until the gelatin is dissolved and the liquid is clear, about 30–90 seconds. Add to the 1 cup orange juice and set aside to cool slightly, stirring occasionally.

    Add the pomegranate seeds to the citrus sections and gently toss to combine. Pile the mixture evenly into the loaf pan, leaving behind any extra juices. Slowly pour the warm (not hot) gelatin liquid over the sections. Tap the loaf pan gently on the counter to release any air bubbles. Refrigerate until the top is set and then cover with plastic wrap. Refrigerate until firm, about 6 hours, or for up to 2 days.

    To serve, run a small knife between the gelatin and the loaf pan and dip the bottom of the pan into warm water for about 1 minute. Quickly invert onto a flat serving plate and shake gently to loosen the terrine. Cut into 1-inch slices. Serves 8–10.

Nutritional info: Calories: 94; Total Fat: 0g; Protein: 1.7g; Carbohydrates: 23.4g; Sugars: 18g.

(C) (F) (TA)

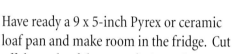

TIP ·····

This recipe may sound complicated, but it's really a glorified fresh fruit jello mold. It would not be suited for someone with mouth sores, difficulty swallowing or neutropenia, but it's packed full of vitamin C and the citrus and sweet combination can help impaired taste buds. Fresh pomegranate seeds are available in the produce department of many grocery stores, but dried cranberries can also be substituted.

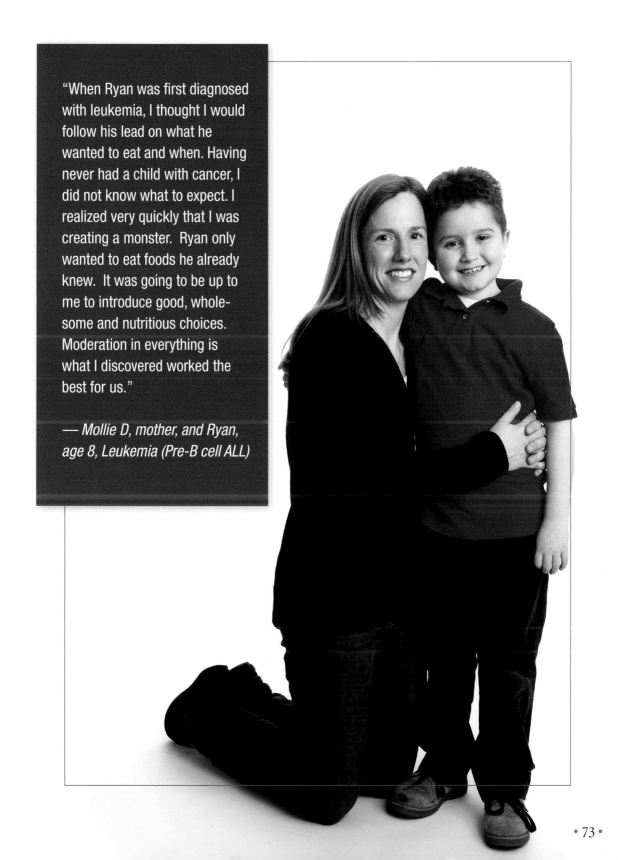

"When Ryan was first diagnosed with leukemia, I thought I would follow his lead on what he wanted to eat and when. Having never had a child with cancer, I did not know what to expect. I realized very quickly that I was creating a monster. Ryan only wanted to eat foods he already knew. It was going to be up to me to introduce good, whole-some and nutritious choices. Moderation in everything is what I discovered worked the best for us."

— *Mollie D, mother, and Ryan, age 8, Leukemia (Pre-B cell ALL)*

Cross-Reference Chart

	Nausea/Appetite Loss (N/AL)	Constipation (C)	Mouth Sores, Difficulty Swallowing (MS/DS)	Fatigue (F)	Neutropenia (N)	Taste Alterations (TA)	Page number(s)
Asparagus Pesto, Awesome	●		●	●			37
Basil Pesto, Fabien's Classic				●		●	36
Beet, Tomato and Watermelon Salad with Almonds		●		●		●	62
Berry Sauce, Very		●		●	●	●	69
Butternut Squash with Ginger-Garlic Sauté	●	●		●	●	●	58
Carrot Coconut Walnut Muffins		●		●		●	60
Carrot Salad, Shredded Lemony		●		●		●	19
Chicken Broth, Homemade	●	●	●	●	●	●	66
Chicken Noodle Soup, Kids' Favorite	●	●	●	●	●	●	26
Chocolate Chip Cookies				●	●	●	27
Citrus and Pomegranate Terrine		●		●		●	72
Cucumber Raita, Traditional	●		●	●			21
Dill-Yogurt Sauce			●	●	●		42
Ginger or Galangal Ale	●				●	●	11
Green Beans, Perfect		●		●	●	●	59
Hazelnut Chocolate Chip Brownies		●		●	●	●	68
Honeydew Lime Cooler	●				●	●	13
Lemon-Lime Yogurt Muffins	●	●		●	●	●	18
Mango Lassi	●		●	●	●		9
Meatballs, Italian and Terrific Tomato Sauce				●	●	●	38–39
Noodles, "Open Sesame"				●	●	●	54
Orange-Cream Freeze	●				●	●	14

	Nausea/Appetite Loss (N/AL)	Constipation (C)	Mouth Sores, Difficulty Swallowing (MS/DS)	Fatigue (F)	Neutropenia (N)	Taste Alterations (TA)	Page number(s)
Peanut Butter Dip, with Fruit and Veggie Stix		●		●		●	22
Popovers, Savory Crustless			●	●	●		20
Potato Salad with Olive and Mint Pesto, Roasted	●		●	●	●	●	50–51
Potatoes, Oven-Roasted	●		●	●	●	●	49
Potatoes, Fluffy Mashed with Poached Egg	●	●	●	●	●	●	52
Pumpkin Molasses Pie	●	●	●	●	●	●	70
Purple Power Smoothie	●		●	●			8
Raspberry Nectarine Pecan Crumble	●	●	●	●	●	●	67
Red Beans and Rice Soup	●	●	●	●	●	●	31
Rice, Basic Steamed	●		●	●	●	●	47
Rice Pudding, Comforting	●		●	●	●		71
Salmon, baked or poached			●	●	●		42
Strawberry Banana Smoothie	●		●	●			10
Sweet Potato Fries		●	●	●	●		41
Sweet Potatoes with Creamy Miso Dressing	●		●	●			41
Tomato Soup, Creamy	●	●	●	●	●	●	28–29
Triple Squash Soup	●	●	●	●	●	●	30
Turkey Burgers				●	●		40
Watermelon Gazpacho, Zesty	●	●	●	●		●	32
Watermelon Slushie	●	●		●	●	●	12
Zucchini "a la Crème'		●	●	●	●		61

Suggestions to Treat Side Effects

FOR NAUSEA, MOUTH SORES AND FATIGUE

NAUSEA: lemon, lime, ginger, peppermint, plain yogurt, chicken and vegetable broth, broth-based soups, baked potatoes, rice and rice pudding are all appropriate foods for a nauseous stomach. Eating small amounts of food as often as possible is really helpful to stabilize and even overt the feeling of nausea. Dehydration is common with vomiting so replenishing fluids is very important.

MOUTH SORES: omit spicy, acidic and gingery foods! Chicken or vegetable broths, cucumber, avocado, all potatoes, oatmeal, carrots and cooling watermelon can bring relief to sores. Smoothies made with peaches, papaya, mango and/or coconut are less acidic-tasting and quite soothing.

FATIGUE: there just isn't anything more nourishing than rebuilding strength with homemade broths such as chicken, vegetable or beef. Soups made from these broths are even more beneficial when adding barley, navy beans, lentils, chickpeas and vegetables.

FOR DIARRHEA AND CONSTIPATION

DIARRHEA: applesauce, oatmeal (soluble fiber helps to bind water in the stool) and easy-to-digest foods such as rice, mashed potatoes, plain yogurt and bananas (for potassium loss) can help the effects of diarrhea. Limit dairy products, but fermented yogurt drinks such as kefir can be very beneficial. Clear-fluid liquids are important to have throughout the day with the exception of apple juice, which can worsen diarrhea. Foods to avoid include high-fiber food such as beans, whole grains, raw fruits and vegetables, fried or greasy foods, and spicy and sugared foods.

CONSTIPATION: pain and nausea medications as well as chemotherapy can cause constipation, at times quite severely. Dehydration and changes in eating habits can also contribute to the issue. High-fiber foods are critically important to bring relief—foods such as raw and cooked fruits and vegetables with skin/peel on, beans and legumes, dried fruits (prunes, raisins, apricots), whole grain cereals, breads and pastas and brown rice. Proper hydration is equally important as well as sipping warm fluids throughout the day.

Ashley, Zoe, Bridget and Bella

FOR NEUTROPENIA

NEUTROPENIA: as the treatment takes effect, the body's immune system will weaken and the neutrophils (white blood cells) will reach abnormally low levels. This stage is referred to as "neutropenic" and is an indicator that the treatment is working. It also adds another level of concern for the patient's immune compromised condition. One way to manage low blood counts is to implement a diet that limits certain types of food to control exposure to bacteria. This is referred to as a neutropenic diet. Sometimes foods and beverages carry unwanted bacteria and potentially harmful organisms that can be detrimental to the patient. When the patient is neutropenic, omit all **RAW** fruits and vegetables while blood counts are very low. Nutritious soups (and more soups!) are an excellent way to rebuild strength and immunity until cell counts improve. Creamy soups, bean soups, brothy soups and homemade broths should all be on the list. Steamed, roasted and baked vegetables, stewed fruits, whole grain muffins with nuts and dried fruits, rice puddings and custards can be beneficial. Your oncologist will tell you when it's okay to resume eating raw fruits and vegetables.

Bibliography and Recommended Reading

Cerier, L., & Swift, K. M. (2010). *Gluten-free Recipes for the Conscious Cook: A Seasonal, Vegetarian Cookbook.* Oakland, CA: New Harbinger Publications.

Katz, R., & Edelson, M. (2009). *The Cancer-fighting Kitchen: Nourishing Big-flavor Recipes for Cancer Treatment and Recovery.* Berkeley: Celestial Arts.

Kornfeld, M. (2005). *The Healthy Hedonist: More than 200 Delectable Flexitarian Recipes for Relaxed Daily Feasts.* New York: Simon & Schuster.

Lipski, E. (2012). *Digestive Wellness.* 4th Edition. New York: McGraw-Hill.

Mateljan, G. (2007). *The World's Healthiest Foods: Essential Guide for the Healthiest Way of Eating.* Seattle, WA: George Mateljan Foundation.

Devan, Ryan and Sophie

Index

A

appetite loss, recipe chart, 74
Asparagus Pesto, Awesome, 37

B

Basil Pesto, Fabien's Classic, 36
Beet, Tomato and Watermelon Salad
    with Caramelized Almonds, 62
Berry Sauce, Very, 69
Black Olive and Mint Pesto, 51
Broth, Homemade Chicken, 26
Brownies, Hazelnut Chocolate
    Chip, 68
Butternut Squash with Ginger-
    Garlic Sauté, 58

C

Carrot Coconut Walnut Muffins, 19
Carrot Salad, Shredded Lemony, 60
Cerier, Leslie, 68, 77
Chicken Broth, Homemade, 26
Chicken Noodle Soup, Kids'
    Favorite, 27
Chocolate Chip Cookies, 66
Citrus and Pomegranate Terrine, 72
Coconut Rice, 47
Comforting Rice Pudding, 71
constipation, recipe chart, 74
cookies and bars,
    Chocolate Chip Cookies, 66
    Hazelnut Chocolate Chip
        Brownies, 68

Creamy Tomato Soup with
    Zucchini Croutons, 28-29
Cucumber Raita, Traditional, 21

D

desserts,
    Citrus and Pomegranate
        Terrine, 72
    Comforting Rice Pudding, 71
    Pumpkin Molasses Pie, 70
    Raspberry Nectarine Pecan
        Crumble, 67
difficulty swallowing, recipe
    chart, 74
digestion: Easy-to-Eat Sides, 45
Dill Yogurt Sauce, Delightful, 42

E

Eggs, Perfect Poached with Fluffy
    Mashed Potatoes, 52
entrees,
    Baked Salmon, 42
    Italian Meatballs, 38
    Turkey Burgers, 40

F

fatigue, recipe chart, 74
Fried Rice, 47

G

Gazpacho, Watermelon, 32
Ginger or Galangal Ale, 11
Green Beans, Perfect, 59

H

Hazelnut Chocolate Chip
    Brownies, 68
Homemade Chicken Broth, 26
Honeydew Lime Cooler, 13

I

Italian Meatballs, 38

K

Katz, Rebecca, 11, 77
Kids' Favorite Chicken Noodle
    Soup, 27
Kornfeld, Myra, 62, 77

L

Lemon-Lime Yogurt Muffins, 18

M

Mango Lassi, 9
Meatballs, Italian, 38
mouth sores, recipe chart, 74
muffins,
    Carrot Coconut Walnut Muffins, 19
    Lemon-Lime Yogurt Muffins, 18
    Savory Crustless Popovers, 20

N

nausea, recipe chart, 74
Nectarine, Raspberry and Pecan
    Crumble, 67
neutropenia, recipe chart, 74
Noodle, Chicken Soup, Kids'
    Favorite, 27
Noodles, Open Sesame, 54

O

Orange Cream Freeze, 14
Oven Roasted Potatoes, 49
Oven Roasted Sweet Potato Fries, 41

P

Peanut Butter Dip, Pleasing, 22
Pesto, Fabien's Classic Basil, 36
Pilaf, Rice, 47

Pomegranate, and Citrus Terrine, 72
Popovers, Savory Crustless, 20
Potato Salad with Black Olive and
    Mint Pesto, Warm Roasted, 50
Potatoes, Fluffy Mashed with
    Perfect Poached Eggs, 52
Potatoes, Oven Roasted, 49
Pumpkin Molasses Pie, 70
Purple Power Smoothie, 8

R

Raspberry, Nectarine, Pecan
    Crumble, 67
Red Beans and Rice Soup, 31
Rice, Basic Steamed, 47
Rice, Coconut, 47
Rice, Fried, 47
Rice Pilaf, 47
Rice Pudding, Comforting, 71

S

Salmon, Baked, 42
sauces,
    Awesome Asparagus Pesto, 37
    Black Olive and Mint Pesto, 51
    Classic Basil Pesto, 36
    Delightful Dill Yogurt Sauce, 42
    Terrific Tomato Sauce, 39
    Very Berry Sauce, 69
    Savory Crustless Popovers, 20
sides,
    Basic Steamed Rice, 47
    Butternut Squash with Ginger-
        Garlic Sauté, 58
    Coconut Rice, 47
    Fluffy Mashed Potatoes with
        Perfect Poached Eggs, 52
    Fried Rice, 47
    "Open Sesame" Noodles, 54
    Oven-Roasted Potatoes, 49

Oven-Roasted Sweet Potato
    Fries, 41
    Pleasing Peanut Butter Dip, 22
    Rice Pilaf, 47
    Simply Sweet Potatoes with
        Creamy Miso Dressing, 53
    Zucchini "a la Crème," 61
smoothies and soothing
beverages
    Ginger or Galangal Ale, 11
    Honeydew Lime Cooler, 13
    Mango Lassi, 9
    Orange Cream Freeze, 14
    Purple Power Smoothie, 8
    Succulent Strawberry Banana
        Smoothie, 10
    Watermelon Slushie, 12
soups,
    Creamy Tomato Soup with
        Zucchini Croutons, 2, 28–29
    Homemade Chicken Broth, 26
    Kids' Favorite Chicken Noodle
        Soup, 27
    Red Beans and Rice Soup, 31
    Triple Squash Soup, 30
    Zesty Summer Watermelon
        Gazpacho, 32
    Strawberry Banana Smoothie,
        Succulent, 10
    Sweet Potato Fries, Oven-Roasted,
        41
    Sweet Potatoes, Simply with
        Creamy Miso Dressing, 53

T

taste alterations, recipe chart, 74
Tomato Sauce, Terrific, 39
Tomato Soup, Creamy with
    Zucchini Croutons, 28-29

Tomato, Watermelon and Beet Salad
    with Caramelized Almonds, 62
Traditional Cucumber Raita, 21
Triple Squash Soup, 30
Turkey Burgers, 40

W

Warm Roasted Potato Salad with
    Black Olive and Mint Pesto, 50
Watermelon Gazpacho, Zesty
    Summer, 32
Watermelon Slushie, 12
Watermelon, Tomato and Beet Salad
    with Caramelized Almonds, 62

Y

Yogurt Muffins, Lemon-Lime 18
Yogurt Sauce, Delightful Dill, 42

Z

Zesty Summer Watermelon
    Gazpacho, 32
Zucchini "a la Crème," 61

"For the child in treatment, food becomes the enemy: harsh chemo twists textures and tastes in a terrifying way. Cooking becomes as important as life itself: the child simply must eat to live."

— Deborah Amey, parent of Kara, brain tumor survivor

"Alex is crazy about the Honeydew Lime Cooler. It is so healthy and easy to make so I keep a stash of frozen grapes and honeydew in the freezer at all times. There are many times nothing is appealing to eat or things that are appealing are just so unhealthy. The Cooler is always a treat, even Alex's friends never miss the opportunity to indulge!"

— *Felicia E, mother, and Alex, age 14, Aplastic Anemia*